FOREWORD

Two expressions dominate medicine these days; evidence based practice and clinical effectiveness. Everybody wants to be certain that the things that doctors do to their patients, the drugs they prescribe, the therapies they offer, even the services that deliver care, are effective. It goes without saying that when drugs are prescribed, doctor and patient must be confident that the best available evidence has been used to establish the effectiveness of the medication. But effectiveness means different things to different people. It is quite clear that psychiatry values scientific evidence over and above any other type,[1] especially when it comes to knowing what is effective for people experiencing psychosis or other forms of emotional distress. The problem is that scientific evidence overshadows what is arguably the most valuable source of evidence on effectiveness, the experience of those who use psychiatric services. This is why *Strategies for Living* is so important.

This report is the latest stage of a major study of service users' coping strategies, and follows on from the work described in *Knowing our own Minds. Strategies for Living* is a detailed descriptive study of a small number of people who were interviewed in depth to find out exactly how they coped with psychosis, depression and other forms of distress. The results are illuminating. Many people are deeply dissatisfied with the way in which scientific explanations dominate their distress. Some find that religious or spiritual accounts are more meaningful. This point has been made recently in *Post-psychiatry,*[2] the regular column Pat Bracken and I share in *Open Mind.* Scientific accounts of the world are not mistaken, but neither should they be taken as the final word. Science is but one of a number of ways of talking about human experience. Each has to defend its own assumptions.

Another valuable insight from *Strategies for Living* is the extent to which coping with the social exclusion of stigma is a central aspect of life for those identified as having mental health problems. Psychiatric diagnosis and medication make important contributions to the process of stigmatisation, and the participants in the study describe clearly how medication symbolises stigma and reduces autonomy. This makes it all the more important that we work in a way that enables the person to retain as much control as possible over their medication. Chapter 5 highlights the value of coming together with others who have similar experiences. This powerful way of combating social exclusion leads to self-acceptance through a common identity with others. The Hearing Voices Network, which provides for voice hearers a positive affirmation of what is widely regarded by the rest of society as a feared and unwanted experience, is an excellent example of this.

In summary, *Strategies for Living* is a major contribution to our knowledge of what really is effective for people who use mental health services. It also provides insights into the things that make it easier or more difficult for people to cope with their experiences. It deserves to occupy an equally prominent position alongside the 'scientific' contributions to the clinical effectiveness debate in the field of mental health. It is also timely, coming as it does sandwiched between the Government's National Service Framework for Mental Health (itself a paean to science in the service of effectiveness) and the introduction of coercive new mental health act legislation.

At the heart of *Strategies for Living* is a message that everyone, especially our political masters, would do well to heed; that the best outcomes in mental health care will be found in a marriage of two types of expertise working in partnership – expertise by profession and expertise by experience. *Strategies for Living* is the definitive statement about expertise by experience, and for this reason anyone with an interest in good mental health care should heed its message.

Philip Thomas
January, 2000

1   Thomas, P & Bracken, P (1999) *Putting patients first* Open Mind 96, 14-15.
2   Bracken, P & Thomas, P (1999) *Science, psychiatry and the mystery of madness* Open Mind 100, 10-11.

CONTENTS

A NOTE ON LANGUAGE

Language and terminology in mental health – or rather, mental illness – is fraught with differences of opinion and ideology, and different preferences for expression. In this research, and particularly in the interviewing itself, it was our aim to accept and reflect the language adopted by the person being interviewed. Hence, at times, the language used in this report will at times appear variable and possibly contradictory. We intend to be as inclusive as possible in our approach and to accept the ways in which people wish to describe and explain themselves. Nevertheless, some terms may benefit from some attempt at explanation.

Mental distress

We have frequently used this term where other people may prefer such terms as 'mental illness' or 'mental health problems' (although we often use the latter as well). We recognise that not all experiences or behaviours associated with a diagnosis of mental illness are necessarily experienced as distressing. We do believe that there is a continuum of distress and that everyone is somewhere on that continuum. However, that is not to deny that there are qualitative differences between people's different experiences that may defy description using a simple continuum based on the degree of distress.[1]

Research suggests that one in four of the population is likely to experience some form of 'mental health problem' in the course of a year. A smaller number will be diagnosed with a mental illness.[2]

Mental illness and the medical model

Many people adhere to the medical model, the dominant view in psychiatry, that there are mental illnesses in much the same way as there are physical illnesses or disorders. Many people find the concept of 'mental illness' a useful way of thinking about their experiences, and many other people do not, wishing instead to challenge the way it encourages professionals to label people within a restricted set of categories and treat them accordingly. It is not our position here to judge these views, but rather to reflect them in this report and to assert the right of any individual to describe themselves in their own words. As we see in Chapter 1, the people we interviewed in the course of this research had many complex ways of viewing and describing both their distress and the resultant diagnosis.

Mental health services

By using the term 'mental health services' we mean to include the wide variety of approaches and support sought, used or received by people, from seeking help from a GP, joining a support group, using counselling and various therapies and so on, to using hospital and other statutory and voluntary sector services. We also realise that many people cope with significant distress outside conventional services and, within the ethos of this report, we wish to include and value their experiences too.

Users and survivors

Most health and social services (both statutory and voluntary sector) have moved towards consulting the views of the users of their services, and some have moved further than this, towards involving service users in the planning and development of services. Either way, the term 'service users' has become commonplace and has a descriptive value that renders it useful to us. Many people prefer to describe themselves as 'survivors', a term that can be intended to mean 'survivors of the psychiatric system' and/or 'survivors of mental distress'. Either way it does not necessarily mean that as survivors, we no longer use services; it can be a more active term of choice for people, more validating, more affirming of a person's strengths in survival. In its roots, it also implies a challenge to the beliefs and practices of orthodox psychiatry. Some people are uncomfortable with this implied challenge, that it is psychiatric treatment that is to be survived, as much as 'mental illness'. For others, that concept is fundamental to their choice of language.

Language in mental health is undoubtedly a minefield, and I hope we have provided a few signposts through it with this brief note!

As Kathryn Church writes (from North America):

'I use more than one term to reflect my sensitivity to the unresolved language wars within what was originally the ex-psychiatric inmate liberation movement, and to reflect the territory in which I work as an activist/researcher... My choice of words is not immutable; I anticipate changes in my speaking/writing practices.'[3]

Alison Faulkner
November 1999

with grateful acknowledgements to Yan Weaver; Making Choices, Camden

1   Perkins, R (1999) *Madness, distress and the language of inclusion* Open Mind 98, July/August 1999
2   Mental Health Foundation (1998) *The Fundamental Facts* The Mental Health Foundation, London
3   Church, K (1995) *Forbidden Narratives – Critical autobiography as social science* Gordon and Breach

INTRODUCTION: FROM *KNOWING OUR OWN MINDS* TO *STRATEGIES FOR LIVING*

'We are all the primary experts on our own mental health and about what works for us... we can and should value the coping strategies we have developed for ourselves..'

This report is based on our belief that, as people with experience of mental health problems (or mental distress), we have our own expertise, an expertise frequently overlooked by those involved in the planning and provision of mental health services. We also believe that we are more than the services and the treatments that we use or receive – that we have a myriad of different strategies or ways of managing or dealing with our distress. The research reported here aimed to explore the expertise of mental health service users in depth and in detail, and to reach a better understanding of what it is like to live with and manage mental distress.

Knowing our own Minds[1] – a user-led survey of alternative and complementary treatments and therapies in mental health – was published by the Mental Health Foundation in February 1997. Over 400 people who had used mental health services returned questionnaires asking them to comment on a wide range of mental health treatments and therapies, as well as a range of other personal and self-help strategies.

The evidence of the survey suggested that whilst many people find medication to be helpful, many have also tried other ways of dealing with the difficulties they face. These range from formal psychotherapy or counselling and the whole range of complementary therapies, through to hobbies and leisure activities such as walking, sport and reading. In addition, the majority of people in the survey reported that they had developed their own personal ways of coping, and two-thirds mentioned self-help strategies. The survey identified three main areas requiring further in-depth investigation:

* talking treatments
* religious and spiritual beliefs
* complementary therapies

The survey demonstrated the importance of understanding the full context of people's lives: how it is that people find ways of coping on a day to day basis, and what alternatives people seek when conventional treatments do not solve all of their problems, or indeed create new ones.

Knowing our own Minds was the starting point for planning a new project to look in more depth at the treatments and therapies people find helpful in distress, as well as looking at personal and self-help strategies in more detail. Funding for the three year programme of work *Strategies for Living* was received from the National Lottery Charities Board in 1997, and it started in May that year. The aims of the *Strategies for Living* project are to:

* document and disseminate people's strategies for living with mental distress, through research, publications, newsletters and networks
* promote a holistic approach towards mental health, taking account of people's mental, physical, spiritual and emotional needs
* raise user, carer, professional and public awareness about alternative ways of living and coping with mental distress, including complementary therapies and religious and spiritual beliefs
* encourage and promote user-led research in mental health, enabling service users to set the research agenda and to carry out their own research.

Nearly everyone involved in the project as staff, volunteers, interviewers and participants has some experience of mental distress and/or of using mental health services. We believe that this is vital in reaffirming our own expertise and in attempting to address the stigma that mental distress invokes.

The work is founded within the increasingly strong demands for change, for freedom of choice and for alternatives to the traditional medical models of treatment coming from service users and user groups.[2,3] It also attempts to address another concern amongst service users and survivors: that of so often being the passive recipients of research as well as of services. We hope that we are making a contribution to that shift in power, both through the strategies and alternatives we are exploring but also through undertaking and promoting user-led research.

The core strands of the *Strategies for Living* project are:

Qualitative research study
Following on from the *Knowing our own Minds* survey, the qualitative research study reported here aimed to investigate issues identified by the survey as requiring further examination. In-depth face to face interviews have drawn out and expanded upon the issues identified as important in the survey, with the aim of discovering ways in which people develop their own strategies for living with mental distress.

Research support network
This part of the work aims to promote and support training, advice and skills development for mental health service users and survivors in the field of user-led research. This is currently being carried out in four ways:

* through supporting six user-led research projects, which have been given small grants by the Mental Health Foundation, to carry out research in areas relevant to the core elements of the *Strategies for Living* programme
* establishing a network of interested service users for information exchange and mutual support, including a regular research support bulletin
* creating and maintaining a catalogue of relevant research resources, including existing user-led research and research training resources, both in paper form and on our website
* publishing a *DIY Guide to Survivor-led Research*, including notes from research training sessions held with the small research projects.[4]

The ultimate aim is to expand and extend the above activities, in order to create a UK-wide research resource for service users and survivors carrying out research in all areas of mental health.

Dissemination
Finding useful and effective ways of ensuring that people get to hear about our work, people's strategies for living and our research is a fundamental part of the *Strategies for Living* programme. One of the main ways we do this is through a regular newsletter. We are also planning a series of publications to tell people about our work, a publication of people's personal experiences in relation to religion and spirituality in mental health,[5] and a report on self-management strategies. We are also planning a series of local seminars around the UK during the course of 2000 to disseminate research findings, and we have several pages on the Mental Health Foundation website: www.mentalhealth.org.uk

Networks and themes
Over the course of the project, we have developed a number of networks, each of which has led to other pieces of work, such as seminars and publications:

Complementary therapies in mental health We held a seminar in 1997 and developed a network of complementary therapists and service users interested in complementary therapies. This culminated in the publication of *Healing Minds* in 1998.[6]

User-led research in mental health Our own work and the research we have supported led to a wider network of people interested in user- or survivor-led has research in mental health. We have a small network of experienced researchers as well as a wider network of people interested in receiving our bulletins 'Research Support News'.

Religion and spirituality Recently we have been exploring religious and spiritual beliefs, with a seminar in 1998, followed by two publications in 1999: *The Courage to Bare our Souls*, a guide to supports and resources for people seeking guidance on religion and spirituality in mental health, and a short report of the issues surrounding religious and spiritual beliefs in mental health.[7]

THE *STRATEGIES FOR LIVING* RESEARCH PROJECT

The primary aim of the research reported here was to build on the evidence from *Knowing our own Minds* and to develop a more comprehensive and in-depth body of knowledge about people's strategies for living with mental distress. The survey scratched the surface of this knowledge and expertise. Face to face interviews with people would enable us to understand in more depth the reasons and meanings behind different supports, sources of help, treatments and strategies.

The aims of the research were to:

* explore people's experiences of different treatments and therapies in depth, in order to find out what people find helpful and why, and to explore common themes emerging across the different approaches adopted
* focus throughout on identifying and understanding people's personal and self-help coping strategies.

The longer-term objective is to provide information which could be useful to service users, their friends and families, mental health service providers and policy-makers. This information could provide the basis for developing more flexible, sensitive and user-friendly systems of support for people with mental health problems, including statutory and voluntary sector mental health services and networks of mutual support and self-management of problems.

THE AIMS OF THE RESEARCH PROCESS

A key principle throughout the project has been to ensure that the work is grounded in the issues considered important by mental health service users and survivors, and carried out by service users/survivors. The process of doing the research has been considered to be of as much importance as the results, and this has meant that everyone involved has striven to uphold principles of empowerment, consultation, involvement, equal opportunities, respect and confidentiality.

The research process itself was designed with the following aims in mind:

* to ensure, through both process and content, that users of mental health services are fully involved in determining the direction and implementation of the research
* to ensure that the messages emerging from the research are disseminated widely
* to document the progress of the study, in order to ensure that the work continues to reflect the priorities of mental health service users and to monitor its central theme: that of empowerment through involvement and consultation.

RESEARCH METHODOLOGY:
HOW WE DID THE RESEARCH

Given the aims of this research project (ie to gain a more in-depth understanding) it was clear that qualitative research would be the most appropriate research approach. While quantitative research (the collection of numerical information) is a valuable means to verify or disprove existing theories, qualitative research is more suitable for reflecting the complexity of people's real lives and providing information which could lead to new theories and innovative services. Qualitative research is a term that covers a range of different styles of social research, which have certain elements in common: a concern with meanings and the way people understand things, and a concern with understanding patterns of behaviour. Qualitative research acknowledges the researcher as having a significant role in the production and the interpretation of qualitative data.[8]

Whilst a quantitative survey can give an overall picture of the size and nature of the issues within the relevant population, a qualitative study can give depth to that picture, through adding meaning and understanding, and elaborating on issues that can only be intimated by a survey.

Qualitative research is indicated where the main aim of the study is to represent the views and lives of a group of people from their own perspective and in their own words. This is certainly the case in this study, where it is the meaning and context of the issues within people's lives that forms the basis of our understanding. As an example, the approach taken towards therapy, treatment or self-help might be influenced by the way in which an individual perceives or makes sense of their own mental health problems; a qualitative approach can establish the links that will inform our understanding in this area.

RESEARCH FROM OUR OWN PERSPECTIVES

As it is still unusual for research to be designed and undertaken by people who are open about having had experiences of mental distress and psychiatric treatment, it was considered important to satisfy two major requirements:

- to produce research of high quality standards acceptable to the academic and professional research community
- to ensure that the community who are the 'subjects' of the research, ie mental health service users and former users, are properly represented and involved in every stage of the work, and their (our) concerns reflected in the research aims, process and outcomes.

In order to make sure the research was done in accordance with high standards of quality in research, consultants from the National Centre for Social Research (formerly SCPR) were appointed, to provide consultancy advice and training to the project.

At the same time, it was considered equally important in terms of the research aims and objectives to ensure that both the content and the process of the research were grounded in the concerns of mental health service users. This was achieved by:

Outreach consultation with mental health service user groups in various parts of the UK
A user consultant was employed in the first four months of the project, to carry out a piece of preliminary research during which he visited 15 user groups in Scotland, Northern Ireland, Wales, the north and southeast of England, and London, plus several African-Caribbean and Asian user groups. Discussion groups were set up with members of each group. The consultant explained the aims of the proposed research and invited discussion, feedback and comments. He reported:

'It was clearly evident that the values and intentions of the project were resonating strongly with the experience and aspirations of users and user groups all over the country.'[9]

Getting the right advice: forming an advisory committee

The Advisory Committee which helped to develop and guide the *Knowing our own Minds* research project was seen as the obvious starting point for developing and guiding the new project. The group was made up of invited representatives from the main mental health user groups in the UK, including representatives from Scotland and Wales, and from African-Caribbean and Asian mental health service user groups. The group continued to meet at quarterly intervals throughout the *Strategies for Living* project, to receive regular reports about progress and to give detailed comments on the work.

Decisions and guidance from the Advisory Committee were considered to be of major importance and generally were adhered to, although executive responsibility for the work remained with the Mental Health Foundation who were also expected to report periodically to the funders, the National Lottery Charities Board. There was a real sense in which the research was owned by mental health service users due to their presence from the outset and their role in shaping the original proposal and guiding the ongoing work.

Employing as researchers and interviewers people with experience of mental health problems and of using psychiatric services

The advertisements for all of the research and interviewer posts made it clear that the posts were for people with direct experience of mental distress and/or of mental health services. Advertisements were sent out through mental health service user organisations as well as in The Guardian and the ethnic minority press. We aimed to adopt an openly committed 'user perspective' throughout the research and to take what is often termed an 'emancipatory research' approach.[10] This approach is gaining support within mental health research, and is reflected in the work of a number of other researchers and research organisations.[11,12,13,14]

The interviewers

We recruited five interviewers to the project, all of whom had some experience relevant to the project, and some experience of mental distress or of using mental health services. We recruited one Asian woman interviewer and one African-Caribbean man, in order to enable us to match the ethnic origin of the interviewer with that of the interviewee. The interviewers were employed on a sessional basis as the work was occasional rather than continuous, and were given training at the beginning and support/supervision throughout the period of interviewing. We encouraged the interviewers to reflect on their experience during the course of their time with us: to make notes on each interview, to write a journal on their experiences, and to take part in a taped discussion. We hear from the interviewers in different ways in Chapter 6.

Training

We appointed consultants from the National Centre for Social Research (formerly SCPR), Jane Ritchie and Kit Ward, to provide training in qualitative interviewing, and to provide on-going advice and consultancy to the project. As a follow up to this, the first couple of tapes from each interviewer were listened to by the consultants and feedback was given to the interviewers.

The sample: finding people to interview

A sample of 76 people was selected to reflect a range of backgrounds and circumstances based on information reported in the *Knowing our own Minds* survey. The following characteristics were used in order to design a purposive sample (see note below):

- use and experiences of alternative/complementary therapies (to reflect the main areas identified by the survey, and the range of views expressed)
- gender
- ethnic origin
- geographical location.

Note: A purposive sample is where the sample of people to be interviewed is selected in order to ensure coverage of various sub-groups within the relevant population. This makes it possible to identify and to explain variations in views and experiences that occur. The samples are not designed to be, nor can they be used as, statistically representative of the population from which they are drawn.

We aimed for an almost equal (40:35) ratio of women to men, and for representation across six geographical regions of the UK. In addition, we aimed for a total of 15 South Asian and 15 African-Caribbean people, in order to represent their views adequately.

We also needed to satisfy another key requirement of the research: to include people with 'severe mental health problems'. Since this is a controversial concept, we decided, in discussion with both our consultants and the Advisory Committee, to aim for an equal number of people who had received psychotic and non-psychotic diagnoses.

We found interviewees through a combination of methods. A number of people were sought through the original survey. Thereafter, we contacted people through a range of voluntary sector projects, mental health user groups and self-help groups, day centres and a mental health CAB project, all the while monitoring our progress in relation to the desired sample. Details of our final sample of interviewees are given in Chapter 1.

What questions did we ask people?

Broadly we wished to ask people what they had found helpful in coping with or managing mental health problems. The exact wording of the initial question varied according to the language used by the interviewee to describe their 'mental health problems', which was addressed first in the interview. These are some examples of how the interviewers began to open up this area of questioning:

'As we've mentioned at the beginning, the main aim of this study is to look at the variety of coping strategies that people have found that help... are there particular things that you can think of that you've found to be helpful?'

'Thinking now about things that have helped, are there certain things that stand out for you as being things that have helped you cope with depression?'

'The main purpose of the interview is for us to find out how you cope with your problem. And people find different things helpful, and it's really about what, over this period of five years, what you have found the most helpful.'

Individual interviews were carried out with the use of a topic guide covering the key areas we wished to find out about. A topic guide is used as a general guide to the issues that need to be explored with the interviewees, but without a formal question-and-answer structure. The aim of this approach is to enable people to raise the issues that are of importance to them, and to use their own words to describe both the problems that they face and the ways in which they are dealing with them. In this way, we hoped to be open to whatever the interviewee wished to talk about in answer to the broad question 'what have you found helpful in managing or living with your mental health problems/distress?' At the same time we did not wish to miss out on any area identified elsewhere (particularly through *Knowing our own Minds*) as a potential source of help, so our topic guide helped to remind us of these issues.

The topic guide was developed jointly between the researchers, interviewers and the research consultants. A list of key themes within the interview topic guide is given in Appendix C.

Doing the interviews

The people to be interviewed were contacted in advance of the interview and sent information about the project, as well as details of the person who would be interviewing them. It was made clear to them, both in written information and in person, that the project was run and staffed by people with experience of mental health problems and of using mental health services.

Interviews were recorded, and transcribed. Respondents were given a small payment in appreciation of the time and the help they gave us in taking part in the interviews.

A number of issues and difficulties arose during the course of the project, many of which involved the complications of arranging interviews and some of which were associated with the practicalities of carrying them out. Examples of these were technical problems with tape recorders, and insufficient time in which to carry out an adequate interview (see Chapter 6 for the reflections and views of the interviewers).

Analysis: how did we find out what the interviews tell us?

Faced with a large number of transcribed interviews of varying lengths, it was tempting to feel overwhelmed by the amount of information we had gathered! Whilst we broadly followed the 'Framework' model of qualitative data analysis for applied policy research,[15] we also entered the interviews onto the qualitative data analysis package NUDIST. (Whilst we have not relied on the computer package entirely for the analysis, we have found it useful for storing the interviews for future use, as well as for searching for individual issues across the interviews.)

The first step was to devise an index with which to code the information; this index was developed with the aid of the interviewers, in order to ensure that it reflected all of the issues arising from the interviews. All of the interviews were then coded with this index and the codes entered onto the computer.

Then the analysis began for real: a combination of reading full interviews, looking for particular themes and using the computer to assist in locating individual themes and issues. We also referred constantly to the demographic information we had about the interviewees – eg their gender, ethnic origin and the nature of their mental health problems – to see how these related to the overall themes (for example, the importance of relationships with others to people living alone).

One final note about this report. By its very nature, it is perhaps in danger of overlooking or minimising the pain and distress underlying people's hard-won strategies for managing or coping with their lives. As one person said 'I'm not coping, I'm struggling'. We have no wish to overlook the very real pain experienced by people experiencing mental distress or mental illness; our focus on the helpful is in order to enable all of us to learn from each other about ways of addressing and managing distress.

For the results... read on ...

1   Faulkner, A (1997) *Knowing our own Minds* The Mental Health Foundation, London
2   Lindow, V (1994) *Self-Help Alternatives to Mental Health Services* Mind Publications, London
3   Rogers, A Pilgrim, D and Lacey, R (1993) *Experiencing Psychiatry: users views of services* Mind Publications, London
4   Mental Health Foundation (1999) *A DIY Guide to Survivor-led Research* Mental Health Foundation, London
5   Mental Health Foundation (1999) *The Courage to Bare our Souls* The Mental Health Foundation, London
6   Wallcraft, J (1999) *Healing Minds* The Mental Health Foundation, London
7   Nicholls, V & Wallcraft, J *Spiritual Dimensions* The Mental Health Foundation (unpublished), London
8   Denscombe, M (1998) *The Good Research Guide* Open University Press, Buckingham, Milton Keynes
9   Green, J (1997) *Strategies for Living Consultation and Dissemination Report (unpublished)* Mental Health Foundation, London
10 Beresford, P & Wallcraft, J (1997) *Psychiatric System Survivors and Emancipatory Research: Issues, overlaps and differences* in Barnes, C & Mercer, G *Doing Disability Research* The Disability Press, Leeds
11 Rose, D et al (1998) *In Our Experience: User-Focused Monitoring of Mental Health Services in Kensington & Chelsea and Westminster Health Authority* The Sainsbury Centre for Mental Health, London
12 Beeforth, M et al (1994) *Have we got views for you: user evaluation of case management* Sainsbury Centre for Mental Health, London
13 East Yorkshire Monitoring Team (1997) *Monitoring our services ourselves* East Yorkshire Monitoring Team, Hawthorne Court, Manor Road, Beverley, East Yorkshire HU17 7BT
14 Wallcraft, J (1995) *Balancing the Picture: survey of the views of Black and Asian mental health service users in Waltham Forest* National User Involvement Project
15 Ritchie, J & Spencer, L (1994) *Qualitative data analysis for applied policy research*, in Bryman, A & Burgess, RG *Analyzing Qualitative Data*; Routledge, London

PERSONAL AND DEMOGRAPHIC CHARACTERISTICS

We achieved a good sample of people in our study, fulfilling most of the characteristics we aimed for, as outlined in the introduction. The first section of this chapter gives an overview of the people we interviewed and their personal and demographic characteristics and living circumstances. The second section outlines their diagnoses or mental health problems, where appropriate, and goes on to explore the views people had about their diagnoses and about their distress.

This report is based on interviews with 71 people, 42 women and 29 men.

Geographical distribution

We covered six areas of the UK in the research, and the following displays the way in which our interviews covered these areas.

Wales	9
Scotland	14
Midlands	12
North East	11
South West	9
South East	16
Total	**71**

Ethnic origin

As stated in the introduction, we aimed to include sufficient representation in our sample from both South Asian and African-Caribbean people to allow us to reach some understanding of the themes and issues they raised. We did this by contacting black voluntary projects and groups to find people to interview, as well as by recruiting an African-Caribbean man and an Asian woman as interviewers to the project. We were successful in achieving numbers almost equal to our targets.

African-Caribbean	9
South Asian	13
White	49
Total	**71**

Age	
20-29	12
30-39	16
40-49	17
50-59	10
60-69	4
70-79	2
Unknown	10
Total	**71**

Living circumstances

Around half of the people we interviewed were living alone, some of these in supported accommodation, and around half were living with other people, mainly partners or other family members.

Living alone in own accommodation	29
Living alone in supported accommodation	12
Living with family	30
Total	**71**

Employment status

Unemployed	45	of whom 8 doing voluntary work, 1 studying
Retired	3	
Housewife/mother	2	
Employed part time	6	
Employed full time	8	
Full time student	2	
Unknown	5	
Total	**71**	

MAKING SENSE OF DIAGNOSIS AND DISTRESS

DIAGNOSIS

When constructing our sample we had agreed that we would aim for an equal proportion of people with psychotic diagnoses (primarily schizophrenia or manic depression) and people with non-psychotic diagnoses, such as depression. We achieved these numbers reasonably well, as shown below.

Psychotic diagnoses	33
Non-psychotic diagnoses	38*

   *There were a few people in the study who had not been given a diagnosis, but who gave their own diagnoses, such as anxiety or depression.

Schizophrenia	20
Manic depression	13
Depression/anxiety	34
Anxiety	2
Nervous disability	1
Psychotic	1
Total	**71**

Of the total number of 71 people, 51 were taking some form of psychotropic medication at the time of interview.

We also asked people how they felt about their diagnoses, and how they would describe their 'mental health problems' in their own words. As suggested in Chapter 6 by two of the interviewers, not everyone we interviewed believed that they had a mental health 'problem' and so this is an interesting and important issue to explore. Many people only saw themselves as having problems when their lives were affected because coping strategies had – usually temporarily – broken down. Significantly, for some people, the 'problem' lay elsewhere, in other people or in society at large in the form of stigma and fear, rather than in themselves as an illness.

Many of the people we interviewed had come to accept their diagnosis, although this was often after a complex process of negotiation and adjustment, whether within themselves as they came to terms with it, or more explicitly, in negotiation with others. However, some people did not accept the diagnosis they had been given and felt that their problems fitted better under a different medical heading. A few preferred to discard medical labels altogether and used alternative, social concepts to describe their mental health problems. Some diagnoses were more 'acceptable' than others. We found that people were more likely to have difficulty accepting their diagnosis or to reject it completely if the diagnosis in question had serious or damaging images or behaviours associated with it in the public eye. Schizophrenia is the most obvious example of this, although manic depression and borderline personality disorder were also mentioned in this context.

ACCEPTING AND ASSIMILATING DIAGNOSIS

Accepting a diagnosis was for most people part of a long and sometimes painful process, involving perceptions of distress or mental illness and how these related to personal experiences. Stigma and public perceptions of mental illness played a part in this for many people. It seemed that people were more likely to accept a diagnosis if it made sense to them in terms of their existing worldview, or if a medical label helped them to make sense of their experiences and receive helpful treatment.

Acceptance

A few people described experiencing relief, as they felt that the diagnosis offered an explanation of their experiences or symptoms and an opportunity for obtaining the appropriate treatment. For example, a woman given a diagnosis of manic depression found it helpful in recognising the symptoms and how to deal with them:

'It's incredibly useful, because before that my therapist was really quite encouraged when I had a lot of energy and things like that and I felt I ought to be going out and making the most of it and I really, probably, made things worse and now I actually know that I've got a specific illness, it isn't just me being, well, wayward... it's helped me recognise where the illness starts.'

Similarly, a woman given a diagnosis of endogenous depression also felt that it made sense of her symptoms:

'Yes it made sense of all the symptoms, but I hadn't thought of it myself... It just made sense, not sleeping, waking up early and not being able to get to sleep and not being able to eat, being constantly worried about what was going to happen, that sort of thing.'

Reluctant acceptance

Acceptance of a diagnosis was very much a part of the process of accepting, or coming to terms with, the distress or mental health problems. For many people, this meant it was something that changed over time, sometimes due to the nature or degree of distress being experienced at different times, and sometimes due to an increasing need to seek help as problems became unmanageable. The point where a person recognised that they could no longer cope alone was often a very decisive one in terms of their preparedness to accept something about their distress, illness and/or the resultant diagnosis:

'I got to the point where I knew I needed professional help, because I couldn't cope with it on my own. And something had to change.'

People had not always agreed with their diagnosis when they had first sought help for the difficulties that they were experiencing. Sometimes the diagnosis was accepted retrospectively when the helping strategy had worked, another example of the process of coming to terms with distress. For example, one woman did not think she was depressed, but after consulting her doctor, accepted medication and began to see a counsellor. She started to feel better and now agreed that the doctor had been right to say she was depressed:

'At the time I was horrified... But I've realised since that that is actually true. But at the time I wasn't happy with it at all... But I've actually recognised that it is probably an accurate diagnosis...'

'I agree with them [now], it's been circumstantial depression, stress which I didn't, I failed to recognise it at the time. I, er, maybe didn't want to acknowledge it, really.'

Some people retained doubts about the diagnosis they had been given, whilst ostensibly accepting it, whether because an alternative diagnosis was preferred or because it didn't entirely make sense of the symptoms:

'Deep down in my mind I have always had that little doubt that I might not be schizophrenic, it might just have been depressive moments in my life.'

Another woman said her GP told her she was depressed. She had been consulting him over what she thought was a post-viral condition, but he had prescribed anti-depressants. She said that she felt better on the medication but:

'Still very tired and sleepy and things and I still don't feel properly connected... but it feels like a physical thing, it is not... I see a psychologist as well and they think it is a mental thing that I've got, you know, but it feels physical.'

Stigma and fear

Being given a psychiatric diagnosis forced many people to confront the fear and stigma associated with mental illness, causing them greater difficulty in accepting or coming to terms with a diagnosis. For instance, one woman had nursed people with severe mental health problems before being diagnosed with bi-polar disorder herself. She said she was:

'Very, very frightened because the few people that I have seen on long term... were very severe... I was very frightened and I didn't see any particular hope and they didn't offer me any community support or support talking to other people. I felt totally alone and they didn't talk to my family. It was a horrible diagnosis.'

The stigma and fear associated with mental illness could also affect people's preparedness to seek help or treatment. One woman describes how she initially resisted diagnosis because she was scared of the implications:

'... it's only been this last year that I've actually acknowledged that I have a mental illness. Before that I fought it for years and years, um, because of all the stigma that was attached to it, I couldn't accept that I had a mental illness, because I'd heard all these stories about being a nutter and all of that and that really upset me and so I refused all the treatment. And I ended up being ill over and over again, until I got to the point where it was a case of I have to, myself and face up to it and deal with it.'

Finally, on a more positive note, a couple of people were now sufficiently comfortable about the idea of having a mental illness that they were able to express pride about it:

'I am proud to be manic depressive, MD, to me is, there is two lines: one is madness and the other is genius and because I am MD I have got a foot in both camps, so I am quite proud of that.'

And after a long struggle to come to terms with her difficulties, this woman also said she was proud to have a mental illness:

'Having to acknowledge that I've got that, a mental illness, has, has been a struggle for me, but I've, I've got to the point now where I'm happy and I'm proud of it. You know, I don't care what other people say about mental illnesses. I know the truth, and I know that what I thought before was completely wrong, it was rubbish, basically, you know. It's um, I know the truth now.'

DISAGREEMENT AND REJECTION

Some measure of disagreement with diagnosis or doubt has already been recorded in the section above, but for some people, it was more important that they disagreed with, or challenged, the medical terminology used to describe their distress. For some people, this was about rejecting the whole concept of mental illness in favour of an alternative, often psycho-social, view of distress, whereas for others it was about rejecting a specific diagnosis – often because of the stigma associated with it – in favour of another.

Rejecting mental illness

A small number of people entirely rejected the idea that they had a 'mental illness' or mental health problem, usually because their own understanding of the problems they were experiencing did not accord with an illness model. One or two were quite angry and resentful about what they had experienced. For example, the woman quoted below said she was 'supposed to be a schizophrenic – that was their diagnosis.' She explained why she didn't agree:

'Just because I was shouting in the street, I don't really feel that makes me mentally ill, but I was homeless... I had nowhere to live... I feel, well, that the way that I was taken into the hospital on that last occasion was a bit of a, it was a bit of a cheek to arrest somebody for shouting about God.'

Again, the basis for this kind of disagreement was related to people's own understanding of the causes of their problems or distress, or their worldview of distress. The woman quoted below, for example, clearly had a view of her distress that related it to her life experience rather than to the model she had been presented with:

'I just don't think I've got a mental health problem. I've got problems, which, um, things, things that have affected me. Made me the way I am. But it's because of things that have happened, that have made me who I am, not because I've got a chemical imbalance in my brain.'

This view was common amongst people who clearly attributed their problems to life events or experiences, or the circumstances they found themselves in, such as the homelessness of the first person quoted above. Two people, for example, attributed their problems to their sexuality – either coming to terms with being gay themselves, or facing that difficulty in others:

'I am fully accepting of the fact I am gay, I am happy in my own way to be me, the problem started with the fact that everyone else does not seem to be very accepting of that, that is where the problem starts.'

Most of the South Asian women in the study took this kind of approach, for the most part seeing themselves as having family problems and not seeing their resultant distress as an illness. This supports the findings of a recent study looking at young Asian women who self-harm.[1] Many of these women talked about difficult relationships and the role of women within the family, and difficulty in communicating distress within the family, resulting in the need to look outside it for support, despite the shame that might entail.

Rejecting individual diagnoses

Disagreement with individual diagnoses was also frequently associated with people's understanding of their distress and the causes of their problems, and whether or not this understanding was congruent with the diagnosis they were given:

'Personally I just felt I was a bad tempered person, but the doctors at the hospital have said that is schizophrenic more than bad tempered – because when I am in a temper I do get out of control, and they classified that as schizophrenic.'

Some people's feelings about their diagnosis were strongly influenced by the stigma or fear associated with that diagnosis, causing them to reject it in favour of another, less frightening and perhaps more acceptable, diagnosis. This reaction was most commonly found in relation to schizophrenia, although also mentioned in relation to borderline personality disorder.

People commonly perceived a hierarchy of diagnostic labels. Schizophrenia and manic depression were seen as more serious than other diagnoses, a point illustrated by one woman who said she did not have 'such a serious problem as manic depression or schizophrenia; just a breakdown.' It appeared to help some people to feel that their problems were not too serious, but 'just' a breakdown. The concept of a hierarchy of diagnoses with schizophrenia as the worst, undoubtedly underlay many people's preference for an alternative label; people who were seeking an alternative diagnosis were almost always seeking an alternative to schizophrenia:

'Well I personally feel that my case is like depression – I don't think it is schizophrenia, I feel it is depression or manic depression that I have been going through... I don't relate my behaviour with the behaviour of members who have claimed to be schizophrenic.'

Several people demonstrated a fairly sophisticated understanding of the different diagnoses, and a definite preference for one over another:

'I think I'm more prone to, I think I'm more manic depressive, moods or mood swings than schizophrenic, because er, I don't hear voices telling me to do anything or er, not in my head I don't.'

In accordance with studies that have explored the prevalence of diagnoses in relation to different minority ethnic groups, many of the African-Caribbean men in our study had been given a diagnosis of schizophrenia. One or two expressed their awareness of the additional stigma associated with this situation only too clearly:

'People think I'm different and will kill them or whatever.'

It is pertinent in this respect to consider the response of one man to receiving a diagnosis of schizophrenia: initially prepared to accept help, the doctor telling him he was schizophrenic made him angry, and he temporarily rejected the help on offer.

Multiple diagnoses
There were a few people in the study who had been given a number of different diagnoses, and who expressed a complete disrespect for the whole process of diagnosis and the people carrying it out:

'... saying oh, you're manic depressive one minute, schizo the next. I wish they'd make their minds up.'

'Well my sick note usually goes down as depression and anxiety... But I also have lots of the characteristics of schizophrenia... I've also been classed as borderline personality disorder, so the short answer is, um, no-one's got the least idea... I would say that I'm chronically depressed.'

Negotiating diagnosis

One or two people had challenged their diagnosis and succeeded in having it changed, whether permanently or simply for the purposes of a medical certificate. Thus one woman had not accepted a diagnosis of borderline personality disorder because she felt this had more to do with the dynamic between herself and the worker she was seeing than to the reality of her problems. When she saw a different doctor, she was able to negotiate the diagnosis and get it changed. She accepted a revised label of chronic depression because she felt it was 'pretty realistic'. In other words, this made sense to her in terms of her own understanding of her life events.

Another woman had a good relationship with her doctor and he was sensitive to her feelings about being diagnosed with manic depression. She described how she was able to negotiate with him to find a written label that she was more comfortable with:

'I'm upset about it [the diagnosis], but there's nothing I can do about it... [I asked] doctor... not to put manic depression on it and he put nervous disability on it. And I says, that sounds a bit better.'

CONCLUSIONS AND RECOMMENDATIONS

The ways in which people made sense of their diagnosis and distress demonstrate the powerful role that stigma and discrimination play in the personal and public acknowledgement of mental distress. A diagnosis of mental illness can bring with it unacceptably negative images of personality and behaviour, with conseqences for people's preparedness to seek or accept help or treatment. The stigma and discrimination associated with a diagnosis of mental illness is complicated for black and minority ethnic people,[2] and lesbians and gay men[3] – both because of social attitudes and because of peer pressure or discrimination within these groups.

In addition, the medical model is insufficient on its own to account for the ways in which people understand their own distress, which are often complex and take into account a range of social, personal and other factors. There are many personal accounts now that testify to the complexity of people's lives and their ability to find their own understandings of distress.[4] It is the responsibility of mental health professionals to listen to people's accounts and to 'bear witness', before – or perhaps instead of – forming an opinion as to diagnosis. People are more likely to accept a diagnosis if it is congruent with the understanding they have of their own distress, and if it leads to helpful treatment.

RECOMMENDATIONS

We recommend that

- **the Government, in policy statements, emphasise the health and well-being of people with mental health problems, and give more resources to addressing the stigma and discrimination associated with mental illness through both local and national initiatives**
- **all mental health charities and public bodies address the need to reduce stigma and discrimination associated with mental illness**
- **training for all mental health workers (psychiatrists, social workers, mental health nurses) acknowledge explicitly the stigma and discrimination associated with a diagnosis of mental illness**
- **training for all mental health professionals emphasises a needs and strengths-led approach, rather than a diagnosis-led approach to mental health care and treatment**
- **all mental health professionals make listening to people's own stories and the sense that they make of their own distress a priority in establishing a relationship with them.**

1 Yazdani, A (1998) *Young Asian Women and Self-Harm* Newham Innercity Multifund and Newham Asian Women's Project, London
2 See: Fernando, S (1991) *Mental Health, Race and Culture* Macmillan/Mind Publications, Basingstoke
3 See: MacFarlane, L (1998) *Diagnosis: Homophobic* PACE, London
4 See, for example: Read, J and Reynolds, J (eds) (1996) *Speaking our Minds: An Anthology* Macmillan Press Ltd, London, and Mental Health Foundation (1999) *The Courage to Bare our Souls* Mental Health Foundation, London

CHAPTER 1

Relationships and informal support

INTRODUCTION

As for most people, relationships with others played a key role in the lives of the people we interviewed. For many people, the relationships they formed with others, whether family, friends or mental health professionals, constituted the most important factor in helping them cope with mental distress in their lives. In *Knowing our own Minds*, the need for someone to talk to or for support from others dominated people's responses to the question: What do you feel you need when in distress? A total of 260 people (about two-thirds) gave variations on this response.

This chapter explores exactly what it is about relationships that people find helpful. It examines the characteristics of supportive relationships and looks at whether or not particular factors are common to all supportive relationships.

It is however important to note that people did not necessarily find relationships with particular people supportive all of the time; for instance, sometimes people felt pressurised by other people or guilty for not being 'well' for sometimes long periods of time. Relationships – particularly intimate ones – inevitably go through difficult as well as good times, and it can be especially hard to weather rough patches if you are not feeling strong emotionally. Many people therefore talked about relationships they felt had been damaging to their mental health, as well as those that they found supportive. Equally, for some people, their difficulties centred on relationships with other people, whether as a result of abuse or early difficulties, in which case the formation of relationships with other people was in itself problematic.

People variously cited relationships with partners, family members, friends, other service users and mental health workers as helpful. Which relationships people found most supportive depended to a large extent on their individual circumstances. For example, as we see in Chapter 3, people who found relationships with mental health workers the most helpful and important to them either lived alone or found their families a source of stress or difficulty. Obviously if a family member was implicated in the onset of distress, and especially if abuse was an issue, people were unlikely to find them supportive.

Conversely, many people found those closest to them to be the most helpful source of support through difficult times. Several people spoke warmly about the support they received from their partners, a few citing this as the 'most helpful' source of support in their lives. Some people were married or lived with a partner; others were in stable relationships but did not live with their partner. Some had been in their current relationship before the onset of mental distress; others had met their partners after they first experienced mental health problems, some through settings like support groups. However, some people did not feel supported by their partner, which was a source of sadness and distress.

Generally, people found relationships with friends helpful, perhaps because they had more choice over who they saw and when than they did with their families. In particular, people found relationships with other mental health service users very helpful, for reasons which will become clear later in this chapter. Many people in this study were recruited through voluntary sector projects and self-help groups and so were likely to speak positively about such groups. However, the strength with which people spoke in favour of these services suggests that their role should not be under-estimated in enabling people to make contact with and form relationships with others.

Many of the characteristics of relationships described here apply to all supportive relationships and are not just valued by mental health service users. What made them so important to the people in this study is that people who experience mental distress are at greater risk of isolation and of finding themselves without support. People diagnosed with mental illness can face considerable discrimination and social isolation.[1] Over half of the people in the study lived alone and many blamed their mental health problems for relationship break-ups and isolation from family and friends.

KEY CHARACTERISTICS OF SUPPORTIVE RELATIONSHIPS

There were many different aspects of relationships which enabled people to feel genuinely supported or to feel able to manage the distress in their lives. For clarity, we have grouped them into four categories, although there was some overlap between them. Table 1 shows these four categories and their components.

Table 1: What was helpful about relationships	
Good relationships gave people:	
Emotional support • acceptance • self-acceptance • understanding	*Companionship and friendship* • shared experiences • shared interests • someone to live for
Meaning • sense of belonging • sense of purpose • someone to live for	*Practical support* • dealing with professionals • domestic tasks • personal care • help managing mental health problems • financial help

EMOTIONAL SUPPORT
Acceptance
Feeling accepted as you are by another person is a fundamental aspect of an emotionally supportive relationship; a prerequisite to forming good relationships. It is especially important in a society where mental illness carries such stigma and the potential for discrimination and isolation. The importance of finding acceptance is one of the strongest themes to emerge from this research.

CHAPTER 2

People talked powerfully about the significance of finding acceptance, both from others and from within themselves. This is not solely a mental health issue and was compounded for some people by fundamental issues of identity: race and culture, gender and sexual orientation. It is however crucial within a mental health context and the effects of 'double discrimination' were described profoundly throughout these interviews. As this man said:

'I am fully accepting of the fact I am gay, I am happy in my own way to be me, the problem started with the fact that everyone else does not seem to be very accepting of that, that is where the problem starts.'

Acceptance was conveyed to people in various ways: standing by them through their difficulties, including them in everyday activities, not judging them or making them feel different and using language sensitively. People who felt accepted were able to relax and feel comfortable or at ease with themselves.

Some people spoke movingly of individual friends or family who had stayed with them through all of their difficulties without judgement or blame. For instance, this woman is speaking about her three children:

'... they always give me a hug and a cuddle. This helps, they don't turn me away. They are not afraid to tell people that my mother suffers from... they don't say mental health, my mother suffers with her nerves. They are not ashamed to say it. So I feel comfort from that. I get great comfort to know that they know what is going on.'

One woman had been diagnosed with manic depression in her early 20s. When she first became unwell, a formerly close relationship with her family was under strain and her father had written to say she was only welcome in the family home if she 'behaved'. She felt this upset had contributed to her illness. Contrasting this response with her fiancé's reaction, she said:

'He was my supporter really... He just made me feel accepted really. That, and I felt that I could tell him anything and he sort of said, 'Well, I'm your boyfriend but also your friend'... He accepted me as I was.'

Some people felt safer getting support from within the family network than from friends, because they felt their families were more or less obliged to accept them unconditionally. This man explained:

'I think family's support is important because your, although you have your friends, who you've made and might have met in the last eight years, but someone who's been around for all your life, you know, you should feel so comfortable with them that you're able to talk about anything, you know.'

Similarly, one man felt his family tolerated behaviour which others would find unacceptable, because of the family tie: 'they're part of my blood'. He described how his mother showed her support:

'Well, when I was drinking she used to take me in. There's not many people would take you in if you've got a drink problem. Very few people would take you in, you know. And, er, she used to take me in any times that I was short of money, she used to give me a few pounds to go for a pint, you know. She was very good... she made me feel at ease, you know... make me feel wanted in life, you know.'

This feeling that 'blood is thicker than water' was expressed by several people. Yet the fact of being related to someone was not in itself always sufficient; conversely, it sometimes seemed to people that it was harder for their families than for their friends to accept that they had difficulties, perhaps because families had different expectations of them. These people tended to look outside their families for support. For instance, this Asian woman said that friends formed her main source of emotional support. She described how she experienced one close friendship:

'... she is absolutely my best friend and her love is completely unconditional, as mine is for her, and it has made me realise that just because you are related to someone, they will not necessarily love you unconditionally... I don't have to pretend with her, I am very comfortable with her and I am just very honest with her, she knows everything I went through emotionally, physically, mentally.'

Some people also found acceptance within their local community. This man explained what was most helpful in coping with long-standing depression:

'It is acceptance as much as anything... the support of others and critical support of others – you know, church, family, friends. Even when I was in hospital, if I came home for weekends, I would go down to the shops and people... knew I was in hospital and there was no stigma and I think that is very important; if there is stigma about it, where do you go?'

Although many people felt accepted and supported by their existing family and community networks, this was not a universal experience. Some people had experienced stigma and negative attitudes from people they had known before they became unwell and only felt fully accepted by other mental health service users. One man described how his friends had reacted when he was in hospital and contrasts this with the people he had subsequently met:

'When I was, when I became ill, I found out who my friends were and there wasn't many of them... [like] I'd got some disease, stigma or plague, or whatever. They'd all sorts of excuses: oh I'm sorry but I didn't have the time; I'd say if you think that an individual's spent a few months in hospital, you'd think somebody could find an hour, find an hour in that three months, to come and see you... in a lot of ways, I must say that people I've met with mental health problems, difficulties, enduring mental health problems... are some of the nicest people I've ever met in my life, believe it or not.'

Very many people said they felt more accepted by, and hence comfortable with, other service users than by people who had not experienced mental health problems themselves. They valued being amongst people who had similar experiences, feeling that they did not need to explain or justify themselves; they were accepted as they were. Several of these people mentioned issues of safety as well as a sense of belonging and a non-judgemental approach. Again, these issues were often compared with the stigma or rejection they encountered elsewhere:

'It [local voluntary association drop-in] offers... it's like a safe haven really, from out there. Presumably there are some people a lot worse off than me; maybe mental health problems will lead them to behave in very anti-social, not anti-social, unusual, unacceptable ways which results in them receiving derisive comments and ridicule. They have to suffer all that outside and in here they don't – they are just accepted for the person that they are, underneath the illness. That really is the key to it all here.'

As one person said, meeting other users could be like finding a second or a replacement family, and compared this to the possibility of rejection to be found elsewhere:

'It makes me aware of who it is that has my sorts of problems, so when I do go out to community places external to this place, it is like, I feel shy that I don't want to mix with certain persons 'cause they might get to know me too well and all my mental illness and then break my heart by rejecting my friendship... I can mix with the right sort of people, and it is like it's in the family, or who knows or has been through that themselves, and then through them can offer and support the people who just know the problem and accept it is a problem people have.'

Many people from black and minority ethnic groups tended to feel a greater acceptance amongst people from the same racial and cultural background as themselves. Like the woman who expressed a preference for a black CPN (see Chapter 3), this man expressed the greater ease or comfort he felt among black people:

'When I'm around my own people... because they're who I see when I open my eyes as a baby... they're the first person that I ever loved, you know what I mean. It just, it makes me happy.'

Self-acceptance
For many people, finding acceptance from others was a crucial stepping stone to accepting themselves – as we also saw in Chapter 1 when considering attitudes to diagnosis and distress.

This issue was expressed particularly powerfully in relation to sexual abuse, where the process of coming to terms with the abuse as well as the resulting distress was often described as long and traumatic, and was added to if the person did not feel believed. Finding others who accepted and believed that the abuse had taken place, and accepted the person as an individual, was doubly important for these people – mainly women.

Thus although acceptance was predominantly a quality to be found in the empathy of shared experience, it was not exclusively so. People in different roles had shown people the fundamental acceptance they needed to begin their own process of self-acceptance. Family members, friends and mental health professionals had been there for people, to listen and accept or validate their lives or life histories without pre-judgement. However, people sharing similar experiences perhaps had a head start in achieving this much-underestimated basis for living successfully with mental distress.

Understanding

Understanding differed from acceptance, in that it was possible for people to feel accepted by another person but not necessarily fully understood. Without that understanding, the extent to which the other person could provide help might be limited; thus when people's friends or family understood how they were feeling or what they were going through, they could offer appropriate support. In this sense, understanding followed from acceptance and helped the person to feel supported.

For instance, one woman said that initially her family had not understood her or why she was having problems. She had found this difficult because:

'... it meant that I had to cope with everything just by myself. And I didn't have much time to cope with it. But they're actually better now, than what they were before, they've learnt an awful lot about it and they're more supportive now, they understand... they've made it clear to me that they're there night and day if ever I need them, if ever I'm feeling low I'm to phone them. And that has been good support for me.'

People felt understanding could come from direct experience of mental health problems or from learning about the issues involved:

'I have two sons and a daughter who visit me frequently. That helps with mental health because they understand. You might say 'how do they understand?'; well they grew up with me, understanding that because I was in mental hospitals, I never excluded the children from coming to see me... always tried to keep in touch somewhere or other, which is very hard when you are not feeling so good... They saw me in different moods, which after I had explained to them – you know about that sort of thing... you remained closer as a family.'

If people felt understood, they were able to accept advice and support from people, because it felt helpful rather than critical or judgmental. Similarly, comments which in different circumstances could have been experienced as a pressure, were helpful because they knew the person cared about them. Several people compared being with other service users to being with people who had not themselves had mental health problems:

'Well they [service users] understand my problems, you know, if you've got a problem you can explain what's wrong and they'll understand, like... But when you're out there, they don't listen so much. Outside like... they don't understand you. Normally if you're bad with your nerves you get more depressed with people outside because they say you're mad, you see. And it's a terrible thing to say about anybody. Because anybody could take a nervous breakdown, any walks of life, anybody, it's just that when it's happened to yourself, you seem to understand more, but if it's never happened to you, you don't seem to understand.'

COMPANIONSHIP AND FRIENDSHIP

Companionship was valued by all people and formed part of everyone's coping strategies. Most people found companionship, in the form of casual and informal social contacts, with friends, family members and service users. For others, typically those who lived alone or in supported accommodation, mental health workers such as support workers fulfilled this role to a greater or lesser extent. Good companionship and friendship were predicated on respect for the other and a feeling of equality or mutuality within the relationship.

Overall, the things people found helpful about being with others were: feeling that other people shared their experiences; having people to do things with; and having someone to talk to. We look now in more detail at how these things helped people cope with their day-to-day lives.

Shared experiences

A feeling of shared experience was extremely important to the people in the study because it helped to affirm their own experiences. As we have already seen, feeling accepted and understood mattered enormously and people sought the companionship of other service users because they were empathic and non-judgmental. The people in the study were broadly united by their use of mental health services, but had different experiences based on their ethnicity, gender, sexuality and on specific issues such as sexual abuse. The extent to which people identified with these issues varied; people had found affirmation with people from the same cultural background, who spoke the same language, in women's groups and with other women who had been sexually abused.

People who shared similar experiences made others feel accepted and welcomed rather than different or 'other'. This man is talking about the people he met at a MIND group:

'[The people] welcomed you and it was a different kind of world, you know, because people I used to hang around with were very um... would like to put you down... when I came here, I was very shy for six months, didn't say anything... and one day, um, I said something without realising, people laughed, but they weren't laughing at me. And that's when I started to move forward, it's like, I let go, if you know what I mean and then I started talking more, getting my confidence. I felt there was respect here that I'd never had outside.'

Women who had been sexually abused especially valued being with others who had been abused, both in specific therapeutic contexts and through general involvement with women's issues. For example, one woman said that over the years what had most helped her cope was getting involved in the women's movement. She had suffered from depression since adolescence, but had not made the connection between how she was feeling and what had happened during her childhood. After reading an article in *Spare Rib* written by incest survivors, she became politically active and gradually began to heal from her own abuse. A second woman had also had a long history of depression but was only referred to a woman's group some 30 years after first been diagnosed. She commented:

'... it was quite fantastic to be with other women who had actually the same kind of experience, well obviously all our experiences were unique... I found that talking to other people who had actually – I felt that I was totally alone. You know they called it 'breaking the silence' at that time, they probably still do. It was just that feeling that I wasn't this kind of monster who had this very sordid kind of life.'

Many – though not all – of the people from minority ethnic groups found it especially helpful to be with other people from the same culture. Language was one reason for some of the Asian interviewees, but the feeling of being understood as a result of shared background and experiences was more important. This African-Caribbean woman explained what she valued about the project she attended:

'... there's a family togetherness, do you know what I mean? It's like, sometimes I think 'Oh, if it was a white establishment I wouldn't want to go', but because it's a black establishment, you know, people who've got the same illness as you've got yourself, you obviously want to come and mix with people who've got the same illness... in a white establishment, they don't understand.'

People who felt they had experiences in common with other people tended to feel more equal within those relationships. This was important because people who felt equal felt able to ask for support because they knew they would have a chance to return it; they were therefore not made to feel inadequate or overly needy. Furthermore, these sorts of relationships conformed to people's normal expectations of friendship and so promoted self-esteem. On the other hand, relationships which were hierarchical could make people feel dependent or inadequate and thus lead to low self-esteem. The importance of equality is implicit in what this man said about friendship:

'You can help [friends] in times of crisis and they can help you in times of crisis. Which is a good thing really. Help each other and all the better.'

Another person felt that relationships with service users were more straightforward and honest than other friendships, because you could never be sure whether or not people were just feeling sorry for you:

'They [service users] have been through similar experiences, you know, you feel they understand more. I have talked to some people outside that have helped a bit – just seeing someone you know, just to take me out and things and just seeing people and knowing that they are still interested – well they are probably not, they are just doing it out of pity for you.'

Equality was also important for people in intimate relationships. This woman described the difference between how she felt with her current and her former partners:

'I think being in an equal, cooperative relationship does help, I think this is the first equal relationship I've ever had, you know. Because she's disabled and I'm disabled and we help one another... I think if you can relate to one person as an equal, you can end up relating to other people as an equal. I'm on a firm footing now with humanity.'

This woman's comment that she is 'on a firm footing with humanity' echoes the comment of another woman, whose experience of sexual abuse had resulted in her feeling that she was very much alone with it, until she joined a group of women who shared similar experiences:

'Well, being in the group absolutely, and actually finding myself part of the human race. They're just ordinary people, and the person who has facilitated it all is a person who has been through it.'

Shared interests

People who used day centres or support groups had a common reason for being there, which made it easier to make friends. Activities outside a mental health context were also important in providing opportunities for companionship based on interests or activities unrelated to mental health or distress. Sport and leisure activities played an important role in this respect and we look at these in more detail in Chapter 4. Also important in helping people cope were everyday activities, such as looking after children or walking the dog. For instance, one woman who lived alone had made many casual friends through walking her dog. She described how these helped her:

'You just go out and meet the same people and chat to them and I have just found that all these doggie people are some of the nicest people that you could meet, and you could meet them on whatever basis you want to. I mean, you can get friendly with someone and ask them back for a cup of coffee, or you can just chat to them for 10 minutes up the road... So you don't feel totally alone all day... it is just contact.'

Another woman explained that meeting people who didn't know about her long history of mental health problems made her feel on a more equal footing. She had made friends through the National Childbirth Trust after her child was born and valued both the companionship and the opportunity to support other women.

Another aspect to knowing people who shared similar interests was that they might encourage people to go out and do things when they were feeling down, which helped to lift their mood. As one man said, when you're depressed, you need someone to encourage you – 'physically drag me out' – because it is extremely hard to motivate yourself or think logically about what would be helpful. This might be enough to break the cycle of "depression = inactivity = depression".

Someone to talk to

Many people said that having people to talk to formed a major part of their coping strategy. Distinctions were made between talk that was 'chat', talking with close friends and family, and talk which was explicitly therapeutic; for example talking with a counsellor or therapist (see Chapter 3). All three were valued, as they helped people to cope in slightly different ways.

One reason why people enjoyed casual companionship was the opportunity to talk informally with people. Talking and chatting were helpful because they connected people to others and the everyday world:

'If you don't talk to people, you lose contact with the world.'

Being able to pass the time with or chit-chat to people was a distraction from problems and kept people in touch with ordinary events:

'Really, if there's somebody there just to talk to at times, to be with. It helps... I would have conversations about anything, it doesn't matter, just about politics and religion or whatever, you know, holidays or anything in general, it's just nice to have a bit of company.'

As well as needing people around to talk and chat with, many people also found it important to be able to talk with or confide in someone on a deeper level. Thus close friendships, whoever they were with, were terribly important for the majority of people in the study:

'[Friendships] are very important, yes. Because it makes you feel that you're not alone. That's the worse part of depression, I think... I feel totally alone and it's a real struggle for me to deal with that... it lifts you up and you start feeling happy again, and you start thinking, well, yeah, I was having a bad day, but it doesn't seem so bad now... Because without you realising it, that person has actually lifted you out of that low mood completely, you know, and got you back on your feet.'

People explained that because close friends were accepting and understanding, they listened and offered support in ways that felt comfortable. At times, some people preferred phone contact to seeing people in person, especially when they were feeling unwell or stressed. For instance, one man who lived by himself preferred not to let people into his house, explaining that it was the only space he felt in control of. He often avoided talking to people on the telephone as this was a further source of stress. However, he had one close friend who called him nearly every day. What made a difference was that he felt accepted by her and so was able to be himself, in contrast to the much larger group of acquaintances and family with whom he had to put on an act.

FINDING MEANING

For some people, relationships with others were a major source of meaning in their lives, and in some cases a reason for living. The factors that were especially important in terms of relationships included: a sense of belonging, for instance with one's family or community; caring about another person; and feeling cared for or loved by another person.

Sense of belonging

Many people gained strength and found meaning through feeling part of something, or a sense of belonging. In this context, people referred both to belonging to their families and through identifying with particular communities: of service users, gay people and ethnic or cultural groups.

Feeling that one belonged to a group could be as meaningful to some people as direct expressions of emotional support. For example, one man said his family were helpful, but when asked in what way, replied that he hadn't told them much about his problems and they didn't support him directly. Nevertheless, he found them helpful:

'Just by being there... The fact that they're there is support enough for me.'

Similarly, this woman said she didn't feel that her family supported her because they didn't believe her. However, they helped her cope by giving her:

'... a feeling of belonging. Belonging to somebody. I don't want to be totally on my own.'

Some of those people who were not close to their families, either geographically or emotionally, felt a greater sense of belonging to a particular chosen community. We have already discussed the potential for user groups, drop-ins and support groups to make people feel accepted and welcome. It follows that many people felt 'at home' in such settings and this sense of belonging gave them a reason for being or gave meaning to their lives.

For instance, one man attributed his isolation from his family to the combination of being gay and diagnosed as being mentally ill. He spent a lot of time at a day-centre, and said that without it:

'I would be lost, so I don't know why I have become dependent, in a way I would say more emotionally dependent upon [name], because here is a sense of family, a sense of family and purpose and a reason for being.'

Caring about and feeling cared for by another

It is difficult to separate out these two factors as people mainly spoke of care in terms of reciprocal relationships. Caring about another person, and/or feeling that another person cared, gave meaning to people's lives and gave some a significant reason for living. This woman was talking about her husband:

'He accepted me as I was... If I get angry or upset he doesn't just keep calm, he gives me physical hugs, physical love... The love of my husband has been a really big help. I don't think I would have survived... he's helped a lot through it.'

Those people who had felt suicidal at times, said that thinking about friends or family had often stopped them attempting it. Children were especially likely to be mentioned in this context:

'If I took an overdose now, what would my daughter feel, when she came in the morning and found me... That's what stops me. Otherwise, I don't know. There are times when I've, you know, just thought nothing to live for really.'

'I want to see them growing up, you know. I don't want to die young, you know. But when I'm suicidal, I don't think about that, I just want to kill myself, you know. And it helps, it helps me if I want to see my grandnieces often and my nephews and all, you know, it helps me.'

Caring strongly about relationships with adults also helped, as this man explained. His marriage had broken down but his father had stood by him and he now had a new partner who was understanding and supportive. He was determined that illness would not destroy these relationships and described how these, and recent friendships, helped:

'... I feel as if I can't let them down and that's what, one of the things that keeps me plodding on as well... I've got a new relationship... and I really wouldn't like to see the same thing happen again, through being ill. All these factors come in and make a force upon me, to keep pushing on.'

Many people in the study had children, some living at home, some grown up and living away; either way, caring for a child or being a parent raised particular issues. Caring for young children involves being responsible for the well-being of another and when people were with children, they were primarily giving to the relationship, rather than being supported by others in that role. Thus parenthood, or caring for children, enabled them to fulfill an expected adult role, instead of subverting it by being looked after themselves. Equally it brought with it caring responsibilities and a pressure to carry on, for better or for worse:

'He's such a lovely child that I am so much more fulfilled having him. It's what I always wanted – to have a child and a happy marriage and a varied life. So in a way it has become easier since I have had him.'

'I've got to be strong for them, you know what I mean, I've got to be, because if I'm not strong, they're going to go into care.'

Unlike many adults, younger children can relate to other people directly and straightforwardly. They can be honest about what they see or feel without being judgmental, which could be both refreshing and uncomfortable, as this man described when talking about his partner's four year-old son:

'He's very honest and so when it was very bad he used to call me Mr Grumpy Pants, which was like, it said something to me really... At the time it made me quite annoyed but it was truthful. And sometimes hearing things which are truthful is uncomfortable... but on the whole, it's been a positive experience... His agenda is out there in the open and that's really refreshing. And that's good.'

At times, especially when they were depressed, people found children tiring and demanding, and almost too much to cope with. Nevertheless, the same people spoke of finding energy they didn't realise they had, and of feeling strengthened or motivated by the role they played in these children's lives. This woman was speaking about her grandchildren:

'When you feel a bit depressed and one says, 'Nanny will you play?'... [I think] I don't feel like it, I feel depressed, I don't feel like getting up, I wish you'd go away. Then something inside you spurs you on, I don't know what it is. It makes you, you love them so much that you... you want to feel that you're important in their lives. You are an important factor in their lives. That is a great help in depression.'

Yet perhaps it is not surprising that the comments about adult children were more mixed. Some people said their children accepted their problems and were supportive; a few felt that their relationships with their children had been damaged by their own problems which made them feel guilty.

PRACTICAL SUPPORT
People's need for practical support varied according to how well they were feeling. When it was necessary, appropriate practical support helped people to manage with as much independence as they wanted. The kind of practical support that people found helpful included: dealing with professionals; help with domestic tasks; help with personal care; help in crisis situations, such as looking after children; and financial help. Practical support was given by people who they knew very well or had intimate relationships with, by friends and by mental health care workers (see Chapter 3).

People who lived alone tended to rely on friends, neighbours or professionals more than those who lived with other people. Many people received both emotional and practical support from their friends and families, but some felt that particular people supported them only in a practical sense. For instance, some felt that whilst their families helped out with practical things, they did not understand what they were going through. This was less likely to be the case with friends, perhaps because people tended to choose as friends those who could support them emotionally.

Practical support within close relationships

Practical support was often given within emotionally supportive relationships. For example, one woman who had a very close and loving marriage said her husband was also a tremendous help in practical ways, helping her prepare for appointments with the psychiatrist and backing her up when conflicts over treatments arose. In this way, he acted as her advocate, affirming her choices and enabling them to be carried through.

Advice or help given by someone who people trusted and cared about was not experienced as judgmental. Several people described how their partners were able to help them recognise when they were becoming unwell and guide them towards appropriate help:

'She's able to help me recognise when problems, difficulties are arising. She's able to, she can just help me, like, be there listening to me talk about them when that's appropriate... she also can give me a push when I need one, which is important.'

'I think probably he [husband] recognises the signs, as I call them, more quickly than I do now, so if I'm going high, he will say 'you're going high'.'

Others said friends or family members reminded them to take their medication or would suggest that they seek professional help. Delivered insensitively, such advice could feel controlling rather than helpful. The difference seemed to be whether or not people felt cared about by the person giving the advice, and whether or not they had asked for the help.

When people wanted support and trusted the person they turned to, they could recognise the value in being encouraged to do more than perhaps they would otherwise have done. This woman said that her mother was helpful:

'I used to sleep in her flat a lot because I didn't want to be on my own and silly things like, I had to, you know, she'd say, 'Come on, do your bit of ironing.' And I'd, I hated it, I hate ironing anyway, but you know, and I'd, I'd do a little bit but at least I was then starting to do something. If she wasn't there, I wouldn't have done any, I would have done nothing.'

Practical support outside close relationships

Practical help was also given by people outside emotionally close relationships. Sometimes these relationships were based on the need for practical support and there was no desire for greater intimacy. However, some people felt that the person supporting them didn't understand what they were going through, and that the support they offered was limited to practical matters as a result. For instance, this man who was diagnosed with schizophrenia said:

'My mum was helpful, but all my mother ever thinks about is providing food and providing clothes – as long as those are provided, the rest is up to us. So we did not really talk and when we do talk, we tend to disagree and have a different perspective, so we don't talk about our problems otherwise we experience conflict.'

Similarly, this man who was also diagnosed with schizophrenia said:

'My mum was a great help because she visited me, when I was in hospital... she cooked for me (and) my mum's sister come... look for me every day and bring some food, because I couldn't eat the food that they served at the hospital... I never actually talked to her about it... I don't think she understands, you know.'

SUMMARY

The language people used as they talked about the importance of people, relationships and the value of acceptance and belonging, frequently reflects the 'them and us' or 'inside/outside' 'sameness/other' divide created by the stigma associated with mental illness, and with use of mental health services. It reflects the language of children when they discover the 'loony bin' up the road with which they threaten their friends and enemies, but most of all it reflects the language used by the media when they promote stereotyped images associating violence and mental illness.

Relationships and friendships are important to everyone, and we are all drawn towards people with whom we identify on some basis or another: perhaps we work together, or go to the same pub or club, share the same interests or share similar politics, background, culture or religion. The difference for those of us who experience mental distress is partly that the potential circle is smaller, reduced in size by public and personal attitudes to mental illness, and partly that the effects of mental distress can be socially isolating in themselves. A lack of money, employment and opportunities to meet new people can reduce the possibilities further. All of these factors can contribute to the social exclusion of people with mental health problems from the wider community.

They can also lead to the formation of our own smaller 'accepting communities', self-help groups, networks and drop-ins where people can feel welcome and feel a sense of belonging. Whilst for some people this might represent ghettoisation, for others it can be the establishment of a new 'family' network. There is some debate about whether these new 'communities' can provide members with the confidence and skills to re-enter the wider community, or whether they keep people trapped in isolated groups. To some extent this has to be a matter of choice, but it does need to be addressed in order that people who wish to are enabled to move out into the wider community.

RECOMMENDATIONS

Most people survive mental distress – and mental health services – through the support they receive from other people, whether they be friends, family, fellow service users or mental health professionals. It is difficult – not to say, impossible – to make recommendations, or to legislate, for people to be able to form friendships and relationships. Our focus here therefore is on the conditions that can best create the opportunities within which supportive relationships can be developed or sustained. Necessarily, we emphasise the need to reduce stigma and discrimination based on a diagnosis of mental illness, and to maintain those services that create the conditions in which supportive relationships with other people may be formed.

We recommend that
- **Government review or replace the Disability Discrimination Act (1995) with comprehensive anti-discrimination legislation based on a definition of disability that includes people with mental health problems**
- **Government and health education and health promotion agencies support the promotion of positive images of people living with mental health problems, both locally and nationally, through a comprehensive anti-stigma campaign**
- **mental health services and professionals work in partnership with service users and the local voluntary sector, to ensure that people in distress are provided with comprehensive information about local activities, self-help groups and user groups of their choice**
- **commissioners and purchasers of services fund and support local self-help groups and user groups in mental health, particularly those established for black and minority ethnic communities, survivors of sexual abuse and other excluded groups**
- **mental health services (including the voluntary sector) ensure that women with children can access services, either through the provision of childcare or child-friendly services**
- **the Government's Social Exclusion Unit extends its remit to give the social exclusion of people with mental health problems a priority, and review all Government policy within that context.**

---

1   See, for example: Mind (1999) *Creating Accepting Communities* Mind Publications, London

3

Therapeutic supports

MEDICATION

INTRODUCTION

Psychiatric medication is often at the centre of controversy in the mental health services. Whilst it can be helpful for many people, it can also be unhelpful or damaging. Medication (and ECT) has been the focus of concern for service users and user groups for many years now, with calls for more information about the side-effects and long term effects of treatment, as well as for alternatives and choice.[1] However, it is usually the main treatment considered by the medical profession, and people are often offered nothing else.[2] Currently, with the review of the 1983 Mental Health Act underway, there are concerns about people being forced to take medication in the community instead of being free to choose once out of hospital. Research such as this can help to shed some light on the reasons for the controversy and the dissatisfaction so often expressed by service users.

In *Knowing our own Minds*,[3] 91% (367 people) had been prescribed some form of psychiatric medication at some time in their lives, the two most common types being anti-depressants and major tranquillisers (anti-psychotics). The data from the survey highlighted wide variations in opinion about medication, particularly in relation to the anti-psychotic drugs, where views were fairly evenly divided between finding them 'helpful' or 'damaging'. Overall, the anti-depressants were considered the most helpful and the anti-psychotics the most damaging, with the minor tranquillisers and mood stabilisers (such as Lithium) falling somewhere in between.

In the current study, over half the people we interviewed were taking medication at the time of interview. A higher proportion of people with a psychotic diagnosis were taking medication than people with other diagnoses. Most of the people who were not taking medication had been prescribed drugs in the past, the commonest reason for stopping medication being adverse side-effects. Two people directly attributed suicidal feelings to the medication they had been prescribed: one to a particular drug, the other to the cumulative effect of long-term anti-depressants and tranquillisers. The main reasons for choosing not to take psychotropic medication were fear of side-effects, or a preference for alternative approaches, such as counselling and homeopathy.

We were less concerned with finding out about the specific details of people's drug regimes than with their subjective experiences: how they felt when taking medication, in what ways it helped and how they coped with side-effects.

One of the key themes to emerge from a reading of the interviews on the subject of medication, is that of ambivalence. Many people had very mixed feelings about taking medication whether or not they found it helpful. It carried with it associations of long term illness, concerns about physical health and potential long term damage, particularly where side-effects were found distressing. Some people had resigned themselves to taking medication and a few were quite happy about it, but the strongest feeling to emerge was certainly one of ambivalence. For some people it was the idea of taking drugs that was difficult for them, because of the implication of underlying illness:

'I don't think it's fair on the tablets, because you've got to take them consistently. I didn't... and actually, taking medication was like acknowledging that I was ill.'

It was clear that for some people, taking medication was in itself seen to be unhealthy or harmful to health. The quotation below also underlines the importance of mental healthcare workers taking the time to give good information and explanations about medication:

'Usually I like to know what I'm putting in my body. I mean, not that I'm, like, a health freak or anything like that you know, but I'm very suspicious of putting a tablet in my mouth that I don't know what's in it... maybe if I do know what's in it, it's not going to make that much difference, but it would be nice for it to be explained...'

Others were scared of the side-effects, or scared simply of taking a drug that might be mind-altering in some way:

'I realise now I should have taken them tablets in the first place, but I was scared. It's being scared of taking something, I think that's the whole problem, being scared of taking tablets, that's what it was.'

For many people, deciding whether or not to take medication was a process which involved acknowledging that they needed help, believing that medication might be appropriate and accepting the need to weigh up the potential benefits with the unwanted effects. As part of the process, some people had experimented with taking medication, then trying to come off it, only to realise that it had in fact been helpful – or that the withdrawal effects were harmful:

'I had made a conscious decision that I did not want to take medication any more, I got sick of it, and so I went to this conference and went very, very paranoid, and I just felt crap, really... it ruined everything really, because I just could not communicate with people, you see... I was so paranoid that I could not talk to anybody.'

WHAT DID PEOPLE FIND HELPFUL ABOUT MEDICATION?

Medication, as was suggested in *Knowing our own Minds*, was most helpful where it was having the effect that was desired or expected of it, without too many debilitating side-effects. Thus if an anti-depressant made someone feel less depressed and side-effects were bearable or non-existent, then it was inevitably felt to be helpful. The difficulties emerged most strongly where the desired effect was not achieved, side-effects were debilitating, and alternatives, or freedom of choice, were not available.

People used various criteria to decide whether or not medication was helpful. These can be summarised in terms of how they it made people feel, whether it controlled symptoms and what they were able to do when they took medication. Table 2 lists the different factors.

Table 2: Benefits of medication		
I feel: • calmer, more relaxed • more balanced • stable • less depressed • more like my old self	*I can:* • sleep better • interact with people better • go to work	*I don't:* • hear voices • have hallucinations • have nightmares • get high • cry all the time

Calmer, more stable

A number of people talked of feeling more stable, 'on an even keel' or balanced as a result of taking medication. This was important to people for whom the opposite – feeling unstable or unbalanced – was a major problem for them when not taking medication. This feeling or benefit was expressed by people with a range of different diagnoses, and who were taking different types of medication:

'... I'm on, er, anti-depressants and tranquilisers... Yes, it's stabilised my moods more, and it keeps me on an even, even balance.'

One man, who described his problems as being bad temper and loss of control, had come to appreciate the value of the medication, despite disagreeing with the diagnosis of schizophrenia he had been given:

'... since I've been on my medications, I haven't been going so bad tempered as I used to be, in fact I haven't experienced any temper at all... I notice that I am a more emotionally calm person than before.'

Whether or not people described their problems as 'mental illness', they did not want to experience the destabilising or frightening feelings that they associated with being 'off-balance'. Thus, even though a few people had personal or political reasons for not wanting psychotropic medication, they were prepared to accept it if the drugs did make them feel better:

'I don't like the depot injections, but, it keeps me well, it keeps me well, you know what I mean, so I've got to take them... It makes me feel better... makes me more stable again.'

Feeling less depressed

Some people, whose experience included periods of depression, spoke of the significance of finding a drug that made them feel less depressed. Once again, there was some weighing up to be done of the benefits and side-effects of different drugs, but people who found medication helpful in this respect were very appreciative:

'The [drugs] I found more helpful in that, if I stop taking them, I know I feel very depressed, so it does take the edge off it. I feel less suicidal when I'm on them, if that makes sense.'

Feeling normal

Some people had an idea of how they felt when they were not experiencing symptoms associated with their mental health problems, and described this state as feeling 'myself', feeling 'normal' or 'sane'. Arguably, all of the strategies people used were intended to help them feel better, or more like their 'normal' selves, but possibly more is expected of medication in the hope of reproducing this state of normality. A few people had been fortunate in finding this hope realised:

'... they've got me on a medication and it's, it's balanced me out. For the first time I'm actually feeling normal. And I've never actually had a stability.'

(Conversely, drugs that were not found helpful were often described as producing an abnormal or unreal state of mind: 'I don't feel myself, you know, it's like total unreality'.)

Diminishing symptoms

One of the benefits of medication is its potential for reducing or eliminating distressing symptoms, and people were very appreciative where this was their experience. Diminished symptoms were experienced by people with different diagnoses and medications, and different experiences of distress. Although the symptoms themselves might be different (eg hearing voices, not sleeping, crying, mind racing), the sensation of having them decreased was similarly appreciated. For some people, a decrease in voices or visual hallucinations constituted a major improvement in their quality of life, although for some the balance of the experience of side-effects was a difficult one:

'The [drug] has been especially helpful with things I see, because without it I would've been seeing a python crawling around there. I get the odd flash of green and red, but no snake.'

'I think that is the only reason my pills have helped, I don't cry all the time so it is less embarrassing than before...'

'The [drug] is just a liquid kosh, but I will give them their due, it does stop my nightmares, which is why I'm prepared to take it.'

Being able to do other things

A number of people talked about the way in which medication enabled them to take part in everyday activities, or to put other potentially helpful strategies into place in their lives. This might be achieved through the reduction of symptoms or through an improvement of mood or feeling more stable:

'I have been able to work, thank God, with the help of the medication given to me, it just happened to be right.'

'It's made me more able to interact with people without being afraid.'

This issue highlights the way in which people talked of the role medication played in their lives. More often than not, where it was helpful, medication was described in terms of 'background' support: something that gave people sufficient stability or energy to make use of other forms of support, such as counselling, or to carry out activities that they found beneficial, like going to work or taking exercise. Together, these strategies led to an overall ability to cope with their distress.

MEDICATION AS 'MOST HELPFUL' STRATEGY

The view that medication was part of an overall strategy, rather than a strategy in itself, is demonstrated by the few people who had found medication to be one of their most helpful supports in living with mental distress. Medication was never given on its own as a 'most helpful' strategy, and was frequently described with caveats or conditions: for example, the 'right medication' or 'appropriate medication'. People had also experienced the 'wrong' or 'inappropriate' medication so they knew from experience the value of being able to distinguish between them.

One of these was a young woman with a diagnosis of schizophrenia, who gave her 'most helpful' strategies as: appropriate medication, physical exercise and community care, in the form of her CPN. This combination is significant because the physical exercise was partly appreciated for its ability to counteract the side-effects of the medication (weight gain). She was finding the medication helpful in reducing her visual hallucinations, and valued the support of her CPN, because he helped to keep her out of hospital.

Another was a woman who described feeling 'more normal' as a result of a fairly recent change in her medication:

'I changed my medication just before Christmas... I think they are much better than the older ones. These are the newer type so I don't get so many side effects or feel so drowsy... I mean I don't feel as though I'm on anything, which is much nicer. I suppose I feel more normal. Much better feeling than something that somehow twists your brain making you into something you're not.'

INFORMATION

Many people talked throughout these interviews about the importance of being given accessible information about medication and its side-effects. Although the drugs that people found most helpful tended to be those which caused fewer side-effects, some side-effects were tolerated if people perceived that drug to be, on balance, helpful. What came across very clearly was that people wanted sufficient information to be able to make those sorts of decisions. However, many felt they had been told too little about the drugs or the unwanted effects for them to be able to make informed choices:

'I have a psychiatrist, a consultant, and I'll sit down and he'll be quite reasonable with me, you know, talk to me and try to explain things, whereas I've had consultants, psychiatrists, who don't really explain things, they just tend to kind of: 'This is what you've got to do,' and that's it, basically.'

The people who had been given clear information about their medication welcomed it because it prepared them for possible side-effects. There were many more people who had not been given sufficient information about side-effects, and said that if they had known what to expect they would have worried less and could possibly have taken steps to minimise their impact:

'With this one that I'm on now, I see a CPN and he told me that there would be a few side-effects that would wear off. So it was helpful to know that.'

A common side-effect of many drugs is weight gain, which caused particular distress for women:

'I would prefer it if the doctor had told me, yes you will put on weight with these tablets but they never told me, so I just suddenly got fat and woke up one morning and could not get my clothes on – it was practically overnight it happened – so I wish the doctor had said... maybe I could have done something about it because... it is horrible to find out that you are fat, it took me ages to accept it because I would prefer being thin.'

Some people had been badly affected by prescribed medication and felt that they had not been given enough information about possible long-term effects. For instance, one woman had been prescribed a mixture of tranquillisers and anti-depressants for over 30 years. She had recently been advised to come off medication by a marital therapist who felt it might be causing her sexual difficulties. She went through severe problems during withdrawal and subsequently realised that she had been suffering adverse effects whilst actually taking the medication. She described how she felt about this:

'Well I am angry about all the wasted years. The fact that our marriage was under such threat because of this and still is... I don't quite know how it is we are still together. The drugs have a lot to answer for... I was being given two tricyclics which I have since been told is rather nonsensical. And they were preventing my orgasm, which I didn't know at the time was the reason, you know. Obviously when I found out I was in a position to finally do something about it. That was what affected our marriage most.'

Together, these examples underline the importance of giving information and involving people in the treatment decisions which affect them. Certainly, some people did have good relationships with their GP or psychiatrist and actively participated in treatment decisions. For instance, reducing the dose or changing the type of drug could minimise side effects without losing therapeutic benefits:

'I know I have relaxed a lot with the medication and when I felt it was a bit too much, like it was making me dribble and gave me side-effects, when I spoke to the doctor, he reduced it... and I have never experienced those side-effects and I have never behaved abnormal since, so I think it is helping me.'

Also relevant here is whether or not people felt their doctor trusted them to use medication appropriately. For instance, this woman did not want a full course of tranquillisers because she preferred to deal with the cause of her distress rather than take drugs to suppress the symptoms. However, when she felt extremely anxious or was in crisis, her doctor would prescribe valium:

'My GP will give me valium any time I ask for it, because I very rarely do... he knows (it) will last me ages. GPs don't like dishing valium out, if they are responsible, because they are addictive. I, the sort of person I am, would not want to rely on things like that... Once every three months I take one. Mild strength, 2mg – even when I was ill I hardly took them.'

MANAGING SIDE-EFFECTS

Many people also talked about wanting help or advice about managing the unwanted effects of drugs. Sometimes putting up with these was the price people paid for getting effective symptom control. For people taking certain anti-psychotic medication, there were other drugs available to counteract the unwanted effects. Some people had discovered other strategies, such as physical exercise, or complementary therapies that could help ameliorate the unwanted effects. For example, one woman who had a diagnosis of manic depression used a range of complementary therapies:

'Like with the side effects of some drugs you have funny feelings and tinglings and things. Massage and things would help and lessen, but nobody ever offers it to you in the health service, certainly... luckily I can afford it (privately) at the moment.'

Similarly, a woman who was taking a range of anti-psychotic and antidepressant drugs had occasional massages to help her relax because the medication caused her muscles to stiffen and knot up:

'I wish aromatherapy, to some extent, and massage definitely, full body massage, could be done on the NHS... especially patients on high doses of medication that make them all physically stiff and uncomfortable. I think that would be an absolutely wonderful thing.'

SUMMARY

Psychiatric medication has the potential to help with distressing symptoms as well as the potential to cause distressing and disabling unwanted effects. People who experienced bad side-effects were, not surprisingly, less likely to find medication helpful than those who had not. A key finding from this research is that it is vitally important to be prescribed the 'right' or most appropriate medication, if it is possible to find it. Adverse side-effects were the main reason for finding drugs unhelpful, and for stopping them, yet some people who had been given the opportunity to try different types of drugs had been able to find one that was more helpful with less side-effects.

The interviews show that most people wished to play an active role in treatment decisions and were prepared to make changes themselves if they felt they were not benefitting from medication. Most people wanted to be able to discuss treatment decisions and so needed to have sufficient information and a good relationship with their doctor or keyworker to be able to discuss these issues with honesty and clarity.

Finally, of course, many people also search for alternatives to medication and for other strategies which will enable them to live and cope successfully with mental distress, and this is what the remainder of this report is about.

RECOMMENDATIONS: MEDICATION

We recommend that

- all mental health workers make clear and accessible information available to people with every psychiatric drug prescribed; this information should be in both written and verbal form, and should include information about both the potential benefits and the unwanted effects that may be caused by the drug

- all mental health workers listen to, and take seriously, people's fears and concerns about taking medication and about the unwanted effects they experience; and that they offer alternative treatments where possible

- GPs, psychiatrists and keyworkers ensure that everyone receiving psychiatric drugs has their medication and dose reviewed regularly, paying attention to any concerns they have about any unwanted effects they may be experiencing

- scientific and medical research organisation, pharmaceutical companies and research funders prioritise research into alternative methods of minimising or coping with the unwanted effects of psychiatric medication, informed by the involvement of service users

- NICE (the National Institute for Clinical Excellence) make it a priority to establish standards and safety limits for the prescription of psychiatric medication, particularly in respect of polypharmacy

- the Government review of the Mental Health Act (1983) include the formal recognition of advance directives (see note below) for people detained or subject to enforced treatment

- providers of services should make available alternative treatments and/or therapies to assist people in the management of side-effects.

MENTAL HEALTH PROFESSIONALS

INTRODUCTION

This section looks at what people found helpful about support from professionals working within the mental health field; for example from community psychiatric nurses (CPNs), community support workers, psychiatrists and social workers.

As we have seen in Chapter 2, relationships with different people formed a vital part of many people's coping strategies. Although for many people, this meant informal relationships with friends and family, there were others for whom professional mental health workers provided a vital lifeline. Seeing a counsellor or psychotherapist formed a significant part of some people's coping strategies and is discussed in the section on *Talking therapies* in this chapter.

Most people we interviewed had contact with many different workers, from the health and social care professions. Some had a dedicated mental health care remit; others, like GPs, were generic workers. For convenience we have referred to professionals collectively as mental health care workers except where the distinctions are relevant. The people respondents had contact with are listed in Table 3.

Table 3: Mental health care and associated professionals	
Health services	*Local authority and voluntary sector services*
• General practitioner (GP)	• Housing support worker
• Community psychiatric nurse (CPN)	• Community support worker
• Psychiatrist	• Social worker
• Counsellor or psychotherapist	• Advocate
• Psychologist	• Daycentre worker
• Occupational therapist	• Residential worker

Note: An advance directive (also know as a 'living will') allows someone to make decisions before they become ill, about their future treatment. These decisions cannot be ignored unless:
- the advance directive does not apply to the particular decision which arises
- the advance directive is not clear
- if the Mental Health Act is used to override a person's intentions regarding treatment.
Being diagnosed as 'mentally ill' or being 'sectioned' does not currently make someone legally unable or incompetent to decide about treatment or to make an advance directive. However, the application of the Mental Health Act (1983) usually means that an advance directive could be overridden in relation to treatment for 'mental disorder'.

WHAT WAS HELPFUL ABOUT PROFESSIONAL SUPPORT?

The diversity of their roles, and of the people we interviewed, meant that mental health care workers supported people in many different ways. There was also overlap in roles played by different workers, within and between sectors, especially where that worker acted as the person's keyworker. Generally, the significance of professional support in terms of people's overall coping strategies – with the exception of medication – depended on whether or not they had alternative or informal sources of help. However, although people who lived alone tended to rely on professional support more than those who lived with others, household status was not the only factor determining use of professional support: not everyone wanted, or felt able, to ask the people they lived with for support.

The common theme running through the interviews was that adequate professional support helped people to live with the degree of independence they wanted. For some people, this meant living independently in the community. For example, this woman was able to live alone because she knew she could quickly get professional support in a crisis:

'It's just knowing he's there can help sometimes. I do know there is somebody at the end of that telephone. And, you don't then, because you know they're there, you often not, you don't actually need to make that phone call. Because you think, right, you know, I feel safe.'

Another woman welcomed the support afforded by living in supported housing. Living in staffed accommodation made her feel secure and helped her cope sufficiently well to be able to study and hence fulfill an ambition which had been disrupted by periods of illness.

Some people, including all of those living in supported housing, had a keyworker. Keyworkers were most commonly CPNs, community support workers or social workers. Keyworkers were frequently named as the most helpful professional contact, in many cases because they knew the person very well. For instance, this woman who lived in supported housing, had had the same keyworker, a CPN, for several years. She said he was 'brilliant':

'Yeah, really good. You know, I couldn't have asked for better... the practicalities of making sure I have enough medicine to take. To helping me come to terms with my grandmother's death. You know, it's whole range, you know, from the practical to the emotional.'

In short, people wanted professional support to help them retain or to achieve their chosen lifestyles, which for most meant maximising their independence and avoiding periods of hospitalisation. This was achieved in different ways, according to the person's needs and the role of the professional providing the support. The most helpful professional interventions combined both emotional and practical support; people tended to experience such workers as genuinely interested and caring.

Specifically people wanted professional support to:

* help with practical aspects of independent living, like cooking, shopping and household budgeting
* help with symptom management
* provide information, for example about medication, services and benefits.

Before examining these specific forms of support in more detail, we will look at the features common to all professional relationships that people found most helpful. These preconditions led to specific interventions being experienced as supportive:

- the ability to form a good working relationship, based on the principles of acceptance, respect and a non-judgmental attitude
- accessibility: especially being available in the evenings and at weekends, responding to messages and ringing people back
- supporting and reinforcing existing coping strategies rather than imposing new ones.

Relationships

We have looked in detail at relationships in Chapter 2 and the principles of supportive informal relationships apply equally to professional relationships. Good, supportive relationships with mental health care workers enabled people to feel heard, respected, valued and of equal worth – similar feelings to those invoked by supportive informal relationships. These qualities are characteristic of person-centred approaches to client work and the extent to which they were present in actual encounters depended also on the worker's personality and role.

These people described how it felt to be listened to and understood:

'... a young lady GP who joined the practice who has been tremendously supportive and who has seen me regularly over these years and I think it has been more her support than the prescription that has helped... I think the fact that she didn't dismiss me as being a hypochondriac, which I felt had happened in the past. That and she took the time to explain a little bit about the relationship between physical and emotional and mental health... she never dismissed me or poo-pooed me or said you're wasting my time... she believed in me, that there was something wrong.'

'... what I like about Dr X [is] he didn't have that aloofness that some psychiatrists and psychiatric social workers can have. He wasn't hiding behind this psychoanalytical, authority figure, professional; he showed compassion and that was really important.'

People appreciated being treated with respect, as fellow human beings rather than, at a distance, as patients. As was made clear in Chapter 2, an accepting, respectful attitude from others can in itself enable people to feel better about themselves. Mental health workers achieved this by allowing sufficient time for consultations, asking about people's feelings and by establishing what they wanted from the encounter – in short, by demonstrating that they really cared. These are fundamental principles for a satisfactory consultation, yet the way mental health services are organised seemed often to make them difficult to fulfil. People were especially critical of hospital based psychiatric services: appointments were rushed and they frequently saw different psychiatrists, especially at registrar grade. However, the same people often spoke warmly about individual psychiatrists:

'I can talk to her. I don't feel threatened by her like I did with other psychiatrists... she supports me in whatever I want to do, she doesn't, she doesn't tell me what to do or anything like, but she discusses what I feel and what I think I should be doing. Which I think is important. She doesn't judge people. You see, I always felt psychiatrists, psychiatrists were judging me too much. Bit too busy trying to find a way out for you. Shoving medication down your throat without actually discussing any, any real life issues.'

'It makes me feel as though I'm human, I suppose. That they're not seeing me as, you know, this label, as a manic depressive, or a mental person... The best psychiatrist that I've ever seen was just covering for my psychiatrist now, because she was on maternity leave... And, um, he was very good. He was, I mean he spoke to you like you, you were equal. He was just, he made you feel better. I mean to me he was a one off.'

The converse of this was described by many people: instances of bad practice which demonstrate the equal potential of professional relationships to make someone already in distress feel much worse about themselves:

'I've had a situation where one psychiatrist or consultant actually kind of, you know, made me feel inferior to him and as a person I'm quite confident in myself and he made me feel, well, I'm not worth anything because I've had an illness... I don't need that kind of stuff because, I mean, the illness has been detrimental to me already but somebody coming in who's supposed to be helping you, turning round and making you feel you're not worth anything.'

However, some people felt genuinely cared about; this person described how this made her feel:

'... my CPN, who gave me a lot of encouragement and never, never went out of touch, even though it wasn't his, when I was on the ward, not necessarily his job to be with me, but I would say having him was very stabilising... He's like having the best kind of best friend you could ever have, because he never lets you down.'

One woman found her current psychiatrist and CPN particularly helpful because they discussed her needs and shared information between themselves. This made her feel:

'... like I'm being listened to and considered. All those sorts of things that I think are important.'

For some people, it was important that their keyworker or CPN be someone they could identify with, for specific reasons. This African-Caribbean woman expresses this in the context of her fear of potential stereotyping from white mental health workers:

'If I was to have a CPN I'd like it to be a black woman... because you feel more comfortable and more relaxed, for a start, because, well I've met some nice white CPNs, but a lot of them have already stereotyped you as a black mental illness... you know, they can't come on their own, without coming with two people, you know... because you can attack them any time...'

Accessibility

One of the factors people most appreciated about their professional workers was being able to contact them easily when they needed their support. Having support available when they needed it made people feel more secure. For instance, this woman only saw her CPN every three or four weeks, but knowing she could contact him in between appointments made her feel so secure that in practice, she rarely did:

'It's knowing that he's there and that I can contact him any time, I can leave a message or talk to him... I can ring him and leave a message and he gets back to me, almost straight away.'

Availability was especially important for people who lived alone:

'I find it's very important, because sometimes the weekend can be really lonely. Um, very difficult to live through, it can be quite lonely sometimes.'

People's expectations varied with different professional disciplines – no-one expected instant access to a consultant psychiatrist – but if a worker's job was to support them, then naturally, people expected them to be available. A key difference between informal and formal support in this respect, is that it is more usual for (supportive) friends and family to keep in contact with people, either in the everyday course of their relationship or if they suspect they need help. In contrast, unless they are in crisis or on a care programme, people are usually expected to initiate professional help themselves. However, as these interviews demonstrate, it can be especially hard for people in distress to ask for what they need or keep appointments, especially if they do not already have some support to get there. This can lead to people in need 'slipping through the net' and remaining unsupported until a real crisis results – again, especially likely if people live alone. Such situations could be avoided if mental health professionals worked proactively and flexibly to enable people to access appropriate services.

Continuity

In terms of inspiring confidence in mental health workers, continuity of relationship ranked alongside accessibility and availability. Many people said they found it helpful to see the same person over time, as this enabled a stronger relationship to develop:

'I have been going there [GP] a long time... I must have been going there for 20 years. So he knows what I am really like, so I think if I went to him and I was ill, or he was called out to see me and I was manic, then he would know the difference. Certainly when I have not been myself he has made a good assessment of what was going on there, so I feel he would be the right person to have.'

'I've been really lucky to have kept that gentleman [CPN] for the whole five years and he has really been the rock that I've leant on and listened to.'

Different roles and working practices affect the likelihood of people seeing the same person; for example, GPs tend to be in long-term jobs whereas psychiatric posts are often filled by registrars who are in place for a maximum of six months; anyone seeing a psychiatrist below consultant grade will almost inevitably see a different person every six months. However, where possible, people clearly preferred seeing the same person, a point which many service providers do now take into consideration.

Supporting and reinforcing existing coping strategies

Many people valued help that strengthened their own coping strategies; they did not want to be told what to do or – unless in crisis – have things done for them. One woman compared her current psychiatrist, whom she trusted and found helpful, with previous ones. She explained the difference in their approaches:

'They [the previous psychiatrists] were trying to destroy my way of coping with things. And not putting something in its place... she [the new psychiatrist] supports me in whatever I want to do, she doesn't, she doesn't tell me what to do, or anything like, but she discusses what I feel and what I think I should be doing. Which I think is important.'

For workers to support people's existing ways of coping, they have to find out what they want and trust their ability to carry actions through:

'My doctor... said to me: 'What do you want to do?' I said, I want to sleep, I said, that's all I want to do, I want to sleep because I hadn't slept... for 10 days. He says 'OK, I'll give you sleeping tablets.' He gave me sleeping tablets and he gave me my medication and I took off. It's like he didn't say... 'oh rush her into psychiatric ward because she's out of control, or can't look after herself.' He put trust in me and then he came and seen me every single day... he's very good, he's a very supportive doctor.'

'The CPN, the mental health services... they'd rather try and help you fight with yourself, you know, get yourself through it, before they'll put you in the hospital. And if they really feel that you can't do it yourself, then they will put you in the hospital, but they give you a chance first, you know, to try and do it yourself. Which I think is really good.'

As the title of our previous report *Knowing our own Minds* suggests, the *Strategies for Living* project started from the premise that people living with mental health problems know themselves very well and have become experts on their own mental health. This study confirms that when people are distressed, it is more effective – and respectful – to support their strategies for living, rather than to undermine them.

WHAT FORMS OF SUPPORT WERE MOST HELPFUL?

The nature of the support offered by mental health care workers was also considered to be important to people; feeling supported was not just about getting on well with your keyworker, it was also about receiving appropriate help or support. We turn now to look in more detail at the three categories people described: help with independent living, advice about symptom management and provision of information.

Help with independent living

On-going support for independent living was mainly provided by CPNs, community and housing support workers and social workers. Occasional input from advocates and specialist advice workers helped people sort out specific problems like welfare benefits. For many people, medication – and hence psychiatric input – also played a key role; we have looked at this aspect in the preceding section.

One woman had been helped to move into her own flat. She felt this had helped her cope with depression and anxiety by giving her a sense of responsibility; by feeling something was hers, she had more reason to fight and carry on. She described how social workers supported her:

'... [they] helped me fill out all the forms and go to the right people to speak to about getting a place of my own... and how to deal with it and learning how to pay my rent and how to manage my money, and how to buy clothes and shopping and stuff like that. They teach you all those kinds of things, of basically how to live independently, they teach you. And it's been a great help. Because without that support, I wouldn't have been able to have made it.'

Community support workers were especially valued for helping with everyday tasks, like shopping and housework, which promoted independence, and also for just 'being there'. Their support was especially important to people who lived alone or just with young children:

'I was feeling like I was going to go back into my sickness and she came out and she helped me out, you know, cleaning, get my house sorted out, because that's what I was worried about, because that's what, why I was in hospital the last time. Like I said, the house was a dump. And I was worried that if it got into that state again, I would be taken into hospital... it did help and the companionship, yeah.'

Another woman, who also lived alone, said her support worker was helping her the most at the moment. She described how:

'... you could call the office at any time, they have got a 24-hour service; from 9-5 you could phone and talk to anybody and if your support worker is not there, somebody else will talk to you and if they feel you're needing more support they will come and find you. Also... you could just come in, which is really helpful, they are all very helpful.'

Those people who lived in sheltered accommodation also wanted to be as independent as possible, and valued professional input which fostered this:

'... the housing project worker is excellent. Yeah. He really is good, really good... he provides practical help, um, but he, he tries to spend some time with each of us once a week, if he possibly can... that time is to talk through problems either within the house, thrash things out, or within your life.'

Another person also described why he valued his housing support worker's approach:

'If I'm at a situation where I can't manage to sort something out for myself, he'll sort, you know, help me, like coach me in a way, to sort it out myself, with his help like... he'll show you how to get round the problem, so he's very good.'

Thus, irrespective of where people lived, and with whom, the common theme was that support which built on their strengths and helped them identify and work out solutions to difficulties was valued more than approaches which did things for them.

Help with symptom management

Some people found that medication helped them cope with symptoms such as hearing voices and did not need additional strategies. However, others found alternative strategies as useful adjuncts to medication, or for managing the side-effects produced by certain drugs. Some of these strategies are described in the sections about medication and complementary therapies. However, some people wanted medical advice on symptom management and most commonly described cognitive techniques as useful in this respect.

Cognitive approaches were used by some psychologists to help some people cope with the voices they heard. For instance, one man saw a psychologist who explained how the brain worked and how this differed during periods of mental illness. The psychologist suggested that he kept a record of the dates and times that he heard voices. When they reviewed this diary together, he realised that he didn't hear the voices as often as he'd imagined and that his perceptions were heightened because of the way his brain was responding during his illness. This way of understanding his situation helped him get things into perspective and cope better with the voices, even though they did not actually go away.

Some people don't believe that hearing voices constitutes an illness; the point here is that he was given an explanation and a technique which made sense to him and that he was able to use constructively. As we will see in later chapters, other people developed their own strategies for managing voices, such as swimming, praying or going to the gym.

Information

People wanted information about all aspects of living with mental health problems and we have looked at information about specific issues, such as medication and talking therapies, in the relevant chapters. We have raised the issue again here because the study raises general points about the value of information to people and the difficulty many experienced in getting this.

Most people wanted information about their illness, the treatment options and services available. This person's comment is typical; the respondent now works for a voluntary organisation which provides information about depression:

'When I was first diagnosed as being depressed I wanted to find out all about it and read as much as I could, to find out why and what caused it and what would help, that sort of thing. I think it is important. For some people, just writing and asking for information about depression and where they can go to get help, is actually just a small step to helping. It might be all they need.'

Having sufficient information – on whatever issue – led to three related outcomes: it increased people's understanding of that issue, it provided the basis on which to make informed choices and thus could be empowering. For instance, one woman said that getting more information about her illness, schizophrenia, helped her cope better because she realised she was not alone in experiencing certain things. Specifically, she felt less worried after attending a talk arranged by the hospital in which a pharmacist explained the side-effects of the medication she was taking. Another woman who had a long history of depression and was on medication had recently started reading about mental illness. She described how this had helped her:

'I began to be able to take a little bit of initiative in helping myself. Doing things to help my depression rather than just swallowing the pills... And I found, realised that there were things I could do to stop my negative thoughts and try to turn them... was a step I could take for myself.'

Many people expected to be given information by their mental health care workers – about medication from their psychiatrist or CPN, about benefits from their social worker, for example. However, it seemed that very often they did not get what they needed:

'You don't get the information from the staff... you either have to rely on other patients to tell you the information, which you might not want to rely on, or just ignore the whole problem altogether... I would have found it much more helpful if someone had actually sat down with me and explained whatever happened to me, how I had got to hospital, what they thought was wrong with me and how they envisaged life going for me.'

'I just feel people don't, especially the psychologists, they don't really explain the point of it and then they get annoyed if you ask them and they say they have – and I did not think they had.'

Many respondents had had similar experiences. For whatever reasons many people did not get the information they expected and needed from professional workers. Instead, many had turned to self-help, voluntary sector organisations and user-led services to find this information. All the people we interviewed who used these groups were satisfied with the information they received there; some valued it more highly than information from professional sources because it came from people with direct experience of living with mental health problems. However, because of the way we recruited people to the study, the number of people using such groups was disproportionately high and there are many people who do not have access to this information and support. It is therefore a matter for concern that there seems to be such a lack of information from statutory service providers.

MENTAL HEALTH WORKERS AS 'MOST HELPFUL' SUPPORT

The people who named mental health workers as one of their most helpful sources of support in living with mental distress, were people who lived alone, or people for whom the family was itself a source of stress or difficulty. They were in the position therefore of relying upon keyworkers or CPNs for on-going support through difficult times, and valued their availability and accessibility as much as any practical support they provided. Two people in the study had the same CPN and were both very appreciative of the support he gave them:

'It's, it's, um, the ability to weather crisis without having to come into hospital, to be helped through it by a CPN... I find that brilliant.'

'Except for my CPN who gave me a lot of encouragement and never, never went out of touch, even though it wasn't his, when I was on the ward, not necessarily his job to be with me, but, I would say, having him was very stabilising...'

RECOMMENDATIONS: MENTAL HEALTH PROFESSIONALS

We recommend that

- training for all of the mental health and allied professions (nurses, social workers, psychiatrists, GPs, community support workers) be reviewed to ensure that it emphasises the importance of establishing good working relationships with people: treating people with respect, being clear about availability, listening to people and taking their concerns seriously, and supporting people in their coping strategies
- training for all of the mental health and allied professions include input from service user trainers to give a user perspective on the role of the professional in their lives
- training in racial and cultural awareness be introduced on a mandatory basis and fully integrated into all mental health and allied professional training programmes
- all mental health professionals take a more holistic approach to mental health and appreciate that individual treatments, therapies and services may be only a small part of the whole strategy adopted by someone living with mental health problems
- all mental health professionals support people in the development of self-management strategies
- all mental health professionals have adequate supervision to ensure that their support needs within the workplace are met, in order to ensure that they can provide consistent support to their patients/clients
- all mental health professionals take seriously their role to provide comprehensive information to service users on diagnosis, medication and alternative treatments and sources of support.

TALKING THERAPIES

INTRODUCTION

Talking therapies are well known to be popular amongst mental health service users;[4] many previous studies, including our own, have highlighted the interest in, and the demand for, talking therapies. In our survey, *Knowing our own Minds*, 88% of those who had tried talking therapies reported finding them helpful or 'helpful at times'. All too often, however, their availability (on the NHS) fails to meet the level of demand[5] and access to talking therapies is not equitable. In *Knowing our own Minds*, whilst 70% of the people in the survey had experienced some form of talking therapy, this experience was not the same across the different groups in the survey. Only 45% of the African-Caribbean people had experienced talking therapies compared to 75% of the white people in the sample. People taking major tranquillisers at the time of the survey were less likely to have experienced talking therapies than those who were taking anti-depressants.

WHAT DO WE MEAN BY TALKING THERAPIES?

We have used the term talking therapies to mean all forms of counselling and psychotherapy, including group therapy. Most of these therapies were provided by counsellors or psychotherapists, but sometimes by a psychologist or CPN. We have referred to these workers collectively as therapists, and to the support they provided as therapy. Many people did not give a specific name to the type of therapy they had experienced, largely because they did not know it.

Some people found talking to a nurse, support worker or close friend as valuable as seeing a designated therapist. This is obviously important and is explored elsewhere in the report. However, we felt it was important to make a distinction between formal therapy and support from friends or other workers because of the implications for service provision: if people find talking therapies helpful, then access to these therapies may need to be improved. Equally, if people's need for 'someone to talk to' is not about requiring a formal talking therapy, then this too has implications for the nature of services provided.

WHAT DID PEOPLE FIND HELPFUL ABOUT THERAPY?

In this section we explore the ways in which people found therapy helpful under three headings: the process of therapy, the outcomes, and the relationship with the therapist.

The therapeutic process

Many people focused on the activity of talking in explaining how therapy was helpful to them. Having the space to talk, to 'get things off your chest' or 'get things out in the open' was in itself seen to be helpful by many people, although this often depended on the quality of the listening space provided by the therapist as we shall see later. Others explored the opportunity it gave to express or release feelings, to find support or to achieve healing. Table 4 gives the range of responses to this issue.

Table 4: The therapeutic process
• I can talk
• It helps unblock my feelings
• I can work through my dreams
• It helps me makes sense of things
• It puts thing in perspective
• I get suggestions
• I can share problems with others (group therapy)

Talking

Some people had just wanted an opportunity to talk about their problems and didn't want to explore their feelings any further. It was important to be able to talk about things and to release a sense of pressure, to prevent feelings from being 'bottled up' inside:

'... to me it was lovely, because like to go to someone and get things off your chest... was really good. [My GP] seemed to think that there was more to counselling than that and I'm sure she is quite right. But it is nice to get things off your chest... I got sort of everyday things off my chest really. I didn't really want to talk about the inner feelings of unreality, really.'

For some people, the opportunity to talk had a greater significance than this, however. They wanted to be able to talk about things they had not talked to anyone else about in an effort to understand their feelings:

'I felt I could tell her things so I ended up saying to her that I felt I loved my grandmother more than my mother.'

Releasing feelings

Some people valued the opportunity to express or release their feelings in an atmosphere of safety and understanding. This woman, who had been sexually abused as a child, said she had previously coped with things by blocking out her feelings:

'I'd say the counselling's helped me to unblock my feelings... I was ready to kind of look at what has happened in the past.'

Physical ways of exploring and expressing feelings can sometimes be complementary to talking about them, and some therapists are skilled in the use of these techniques. One woman had found a combination of counselling and art therapy useful, especially when she was working on abuse that had happened when she was very young, before she had learned to speak: 'I think that because I was preverbal, I found that art therapy was outstanding really.'

'Talking therapies' can therefore include non-verbal methods and there were people who found this more useful than talking alone, or who found different approaches helpful at different times. Two Asian women used a voluntary agency that offered a 12-week course of massage alongside 12 weeks of counselling. Both felt that massage enhanced the benefits of counselling; this woman explains how:

'I would have the counselling session and go straight into massage – maybe an hour or two later – it was incredible because it was almost like having a lot of the stress massaged out of your body; so having released it orally and having expressed it, it was physically removed and it felt as though – I was just completely lighter all over, and very, very relaxed.'

Suggestions and strategies

For some people, it seemed that being properly heard enabled them to find their own ways to move forward and they did not want suggestions or advice from their therapist. Other people wanted greater direction from their therapist and found cognitive approaches helpful. This Asian man wanted his therapist to help structure his week and motivate him in a very task-oriented way:

'... she would keep a proper file and she will write down the talk we had and she will say alright, these are the things which you are supposed to do between this afternoon and Wednesday afternoon... very helpful... she created motivation in me by using the new techniques.'

Some people found the more structured approach offered by cognitive therapy helpful, saying, for example, that it helped them to reframe negative thoughts:

'It's making me look at things in a more, you know... somebody snubs me on the street, I've got this hypersensitiveness; I think, oh what have I done wrong, she doesn't like me. Instead of looking at the negative, she (the therapist) will say to me: Have you got evidence to prove that? I'll go, maybe not. So she makes me look at things in another way – 'well, maybe you know, they were busy, they didn't see you or maybe it was just their problem'... things like that.'

One woman described how her therapist helped her work through disturbing dreams and nightmares by encouraging her to act them out, so they could explore what issues were involved.

Sharing problems (group therapy)

Several people talked about the value of sharing problems with others in a group – the realisation that others experience similar feelings or problems was found to be reassuring or affirming. Even the fact that others might have worse problems could be reassuring or uplifting:

'I liked the group therapy, I always enjoyed that, because you can pull yourself out there, and there is always someone there who will feel the same or support you in some way, and in fact you always find that there are others with worse problems than yourself.'

Whichever approach people found most helpful, the process of therapy could be hard at times. Several people acknowledged that they had felt worse before they had started to feel better:

'I feel washed out afterwards. I feel really, totally drained because sometimes the conversation goes really really deep. And as much as sometimes I get upset in the sessions, it's worth it in the end because it gets rid of a lot of garbage that I'm holding inside. Um, it takes all the pressure off me. And as much as I feel drained afterwards, it's worth it because the next day I feel a whole lot better.'

'[At first] I think it is not doing me any good because I am crying and crying and sitting there and telling all my things to them and it is not... but after three or four weeks I did feel better then, after the crying and all the things that were inside and which I could not tell anybody, and I feel better then and I love to come back again.'

Relationship with the therapist

Many people talked about the ways in which the therapist him or herself had contributed to the therapeutic process, and had enabled the space to feel safe enough to disclose personal information. Forming a good therapeutic relationship is not just about chance. Therapists are responsible for creating the conditions in which clients feel safe and able to build up a trusting relationship in which they can explore things that matter to them. Different types of therapy put differing amounts of emphasis on different aspects and if potential clients know what these are, and are able to choose who they see, they are more likely to see someone they feel comfortable with. For example, cognitive therapy tends to be goal-oriented and will teach people techniques; psychodynamic therapy is explorative and focuses on relationships, often explicitly examining the client-therapist relationship.

People's comments in the interviews showed the importance of the therapist in establishing a good relationship between therapist and client: establishing such foundations as trust, respect, confidentiality and understanding. Table 5 lists the key statements people made about the therapist or their relationship with him or her.

Table 5: The therapist
• I feel listened to
• I feel understood
• I feel believed
• I feel safe
• I feel accepted
• I trust, have faith in, the therapist
• I can go at my own pace
• S/he is non-judgemental
• S/he takes an interest
• S/he is there for me
• S/he knows me thoroughly, knows what s/he is talking about

Listened to and understood

Having someone to talk to was not sufficient in itself; it was important that people felt listened to and understood (see also Chapter 2). The important elements of good listening seemed to be the communication of a genuine understanding, and an 'active' listening – in other words, a sense that the therapist was feeding back in a constructive way, as demonstrated in the example below:

'It was someone listening to what I was saying without criticising me, listening to my problems and was making me see them in different ways...'

Genuine understanding might be communicated through such active listening, but also might be felt through a sense of caring or compassion:

'She was very compassionate, genuinely understanding, she had had a lot of experience in the field. She just turned around my whole negative outlook and attitude and self.'

For another woman, it was the quality of the response she received from her therapist that enabled her to accept her feelings and lay them to rest:

'It was the way she sort of spoke to me, the way that she came through with the sort of counselling. It was as if she was turning over pages or something, making it all so much simpler in my mind, somehow.'

Feeling safe

Many people talked about the value of finding a safe space with their therapist, a space in which they could feel safe enough to talk about difficult issues or express difficult feelings. Very often this might mean feeling able to be very vulnerable, as this man expresses very well:

'And about 15 minutes into it, I actually said 'Look, I've had this memory' and then, I seem to remember I then started crying. And he just, like, gave me space to feel fragile and vulnerable. Because, I think I've not been able, not felt safe in talking to anyone else about it. And not felt safe thinking about it on my own.'

Another aspect of 'space', and one of the things people most frequently said, is that it was helpful to be able to talk about the things they wanted, in other words, to influence or lead the therapeutic process. One man expresses the value of this very clearly:

'Well the guy gives me space. My last session, which is 50 minutes, I lay on the floor and didn't say anything for 40 minutes and, um, well I mean I pay money for this, but I just felt, you know, I was quite happy to be there and we did actually discuss a bit of what had gone on, but he's quite prepared to actually allow me to do that... it allows me to get some feeling of balance for myself.'

One of the reasons why people preferred to see a designated therapist was because other mental health workers often had specific remits which precluded the space for free-flowing talk:

'It is good to talk because she lets me talk about what's in my head, whereas my CPN, if he doesn't want me to talk about something, or if I go back into the past too far, he says: I don't want to talk about the past... today I want to talk about this. So he sometimes drags me away from past events.'

Feeling accepted, being believed

Psychological space was given in a relationship of trust, where the person felt that they had been heard, accepted, understood and believed. For some people, this was a new experience:

'... you feel brilliant because at least someone has believed you for once in your life, you know – it is just wonderful and afterwards I feel really better and feel confident and I just go back home with renewed spirit and confidence and I don't feel that scared as what I usually am with my husband.'

This sense of being accepted and believed was felt particularly strongly by people who had been sexually abused as children. These women and men spoke very powerfully of the value of being listened to in an atmosphere of safety, belief and understanding:

'... it was somebody who believed me, who accepted me, who, who had seen other women who had been sexually abused, who knew a little bit about it and who was able to reassure me that I was not flipped; I thought I was going crazy.'

Non-judgemental

For many people, it was the sense that they were not being judged or criticised for what they had to say that was important to them. In some instances, they compared this with their experience with other professionals, or with family or friends, who they felt had judged them in some way:

'Well, a lot of what is worrying me I can talk to her about it, it kind of reassures me that she is not judgmental and that, which is good.'

For a number of people, trusting that a therapist would be able to understand them and be non-judgmental, was easier if the therapist was of the same ethnic or cultural background or gender. This African-Caribbean man explains why:

'... you tend to feel more at home with a black person... It is just a general feeling, you feel more relaxed and you can talk, you can be more open with yourself talking with a black person rather than talking with a white person... if I am in a schizophrenic sort of mood or attitude, you might think that this white person can use what I have said against me, whereas with a black person you won't feel like that at all... at the same time a man would feel more comfortable talking to another man about problems, rather than talking to a woman.'

Similarly this Asian woman said:

'... when I came I wanted to talk to somebody of my own culture and my own age and they have children and problems, and they should, supposed to understand what I am going through.'

Most of the Asian interviewees talked about the importance of talking to someone from the same ethnic and cultural background; however, not all of them did, and this was reflected in the fact that some Asian women were happy to be interviewed in the study by a white female interviewer. The issue of confidentiality could be complex; if needing help or counselling was seen as shameful, then revealing this shame to someone of the same culture could be more of a barrier than revealing it to someone of a different background.[6]

Comparisons

A number of people talked about the positive aspects of therapists through comparing them with more difficult or negative experiences of therapists. For example, one Asian woman who spoke very positively about counselling at an Asian voluntary organisation, first saw a counsellor at her doctor's surgery. She did not find this counselling helpful and had not taken up the offer to extend the initial contract.

This woman, who had been sexually abused, compared seeing a male psychologist with seeing a female counsellor. The psychologist had seemed very angry because she had found it difficult to talk and she said she was terrified of him. Finally, when she did disclose the abuse, he told her, with no explanation, that he was unable to help, which 'knocked her for six'. In contrast, counselling had helped a great deal because it had helped her release her feelings:

'I feel safe with her. I don't feel threatened with her like I did with the psychologist or the psychiatrist... I don't panic. I don't feel frightened. I can say, I can let go of my feelings and they'll let me and they'll help me. But if I do, she's there for me.'

Similarly, one woman had first seen a counsellor at her college, who she described as 'dreadful'. The counsellor had disclosed aspects of her own personal life and problems, which the woman felt was entirely inappropriate. She left and found a counsellor through the voluntary sector, who was 'fantastic.'

Some people talked about the importance of talking to someone outside of their family or friendship networks, due to the need for confidentiality. This can be a key difference between seeing a professional and talking with friends or family, particularly for people whose families are unsympathetic or regard it as shameful to speak of problems to strangers:

'I told the psychotherapist because she was a confidential person and wasn't going to tell anybody else.'

Outcomes

We asked people how talking therapies had been helpful overall – what they felt the benefits or outcomes had been for them. For many, this was a difficult question to answer, because the benefits were not always tangible, and were more associated with the process (of being believed, being accepted and understood) than about the outcomes or results of therapy. Table 6 lists the overall benefits or outcomes people talked about in relation to their experience of therapy.

Table 6: Outcomes
• I have learnt to talk about feelings
• I have learnt a lot about myself
• I feel stronger, more confident
• I put myself first now
• I can accept myself
• I am not so hard on myself
• I have hope
• I have laid things to rest
• I have moved forward
• I have reduced my medication
• It helps me manage voices

Learning

Several people talked about learning to talk about their feelings through therapy, the fact of being able to talk about difficult issues or feelings representing an achievement in itself:

'And it was basically from there that I learned how to talk, because she was very gentle and persuading, and I, I'd get frustrated because I'd be wanting to say something, and I couldn't get it out, that I would just sit in silence for the entire session. And this went on for ages and ages, and then it all just burst out one day.'

There were a number of people who said that they had learned about themselves through therapy, learnt to understand their feelings or difficulties and through this to accept themselves. This was often after a long period of exploring things in depth and making sense of what they had been through. Talking about her six years of psychotherapy, this woman said:

'Yes, it was helpful. I think I know an awful lot about myself that I didn't know. I don't think, I mean in some ways I've come to terms with my childhood, my previous... all that's gone on in my life... It was helpful because I learnt a lot about myself... it helped me accept myself for what I am and not think of what I'd like to be, really.'

The women in our study who had experienced sexual abuse commonly talked about finding acceptance through therapy – both acceptance of their life experiences and of themselves as a result. It was crucial to these women that they felt believed and accepted by the therapist as part of the process, and the result could be a real sense of understanding and moving forward:

'What have I got out of it? I've just been able to, like, feel that I've moved forward in my healing around the abuse. I've been able to like, recognise it... a year ago, if we were having this interview, I wouldn't have been able to say about being abused. Or been able to accept it... And begin to realise how it has been affecting my life and how it's affected my relationships, both my intimate relationships and other relationships.'

This woman went on to say that the counselling she had received around sexual abuse had given her hope that she was going to get better.

Confidence

Some people hoped that the changes in the way they felt about themselves would enable them to change the way they behaved; a common goal was to be more assertive with other people. Many people talked about feeling more confident or assertive, as a result of therapy:

'Counselling's good for me because it makes me confident and assertive... 'think positive, don't think negative.' She says: think positive, because I always think about negatives you know... now I'm not like that, I'm not a miserable person, I'm OK.'

Most of the Asian women in our study who had experienced counselling, were particularly appreciative of learning to put themselves first, and to be more assertive in relationships with family members:

'When I came to the counselling, the first thing which I liked and learned from [it] is to think about myself first. I was always thinking of my daughters and everything.'

Through counselling at an Asian voluntary organisation, the woman quoted below had learnt that she had a right to stand up for herself and had become more assertive with her husband. She went on to say she hoped she could take this further:

'... the real test is when my mother-in-law comes over... the thing is, I never felt like this before, I was so scared of her, really really scared of her, but now, since the counselling, it has given me the courage to stand up to [her].'

Strategies

A couple of people talked about having learnt strategies for hearing voices or dealing with other distressing symptoms, usually in this case from psychologists. One person said that she had reduced her medication as a result of therapy:

'He got me into a technique whereby I do like a weekly chart, which you have each day, and the time and duration of the voices, whether they were good voices, bad voices, and then I got into a routine where I just dismissed them.'

TALKING THERAPIES AS 'MOST HELPFUL' SUPPORT

From all of the interviews for this study, two groups of people stand out as having found therapy particularly beneficial: people who had experienced sexual abuse and Asian women. They spoke powerfully of the value of finding a safe space outside their immediate networks, of finding others who had experienced similar problems, and of expressing their feelings through talking and understanding. Asian women had learnt to value themselves more and to become more assertive or confident. Those people who had experienced sexual abuse spoke of the powerful effect that being believed and accepted for themselves had had on them. Each of their experiences is one of isolation and a lack of safety within the family network: Asian women in their families, where either the family is the source of distress or emotional or mental distress is something to be ashamed of, and sexual abuse that often cannot find a space in which to be recognised.

ACCESS AND AVAILABILITY

Many people in the study talked about the difficulties of gaining access to talking therapies, and the need for their greater availability. The issue of cost was mentioned in connection with the wider availability of private therapy, but also the need was expressed for more counselling or psychotherapy to be provided in the voluntary sector as well as on the NHS. People mentioned the easy availability of psychotropic medication in contrast to the difficulty in gaining access to therapy:

'I feel there should be more counselling... I've never had any counselling, no... maybe it's just, I think it was probably expensive and that's why.'

Some people had had to find out about therapy themselves and then fight to actually get it; for example this woman said:

'I knew when I was a nurse that people did have psychotherapy, so I started finding out... So I asked for it, I had to fight quite hard to get it.'

Her psychotherapy sessions had ended and, although she had wondered whether it would be helpful to have more, did not consider this likely because she had had her entitlement on the NHS.

One person highlighted the lack of counselling provision – or for someone to talk to – in hospital:

'I'd have liked it if the nurse had come to me and had a set time with me or something like that... counselling sort of idea. I think a lot of patients wanted that. They wanted to talk but there was no-one there to talk to.'

As has already been mentioned, there are particular issues relating to the provision of talking therapies for people from black and minority ethnic communities. The need to provide culturally appropriate counselling services is well documented elsewhere[7,8] and is borne out by the comments of people in this study. The African-Caribbean man mentioned earlier spoke powerfully of the value of speaking to a black person, of not being judged and feeling more comfortable: 'you can be more open with yourself'. An Asian woman who had group therapy at a voluntary sector project highlighted the need for greater provision of culturally appropriate services:

'We do need these types of groups more... especially for Asian women.'

RECOMMENDATIONS: TALKING THERAPIES

We recommend that

- everyone in contact with mental health services has the right to have someone to talk to, the right to be listened to and to be taken seriously, particularly in times of crisis: this may not be a formal 'talking treatment' but may be the time and the space in which to talk

- access to all forms of 'talking treatment' should be equal: everyone should be offered some form of counselling or psychotherapy – or the opportunity to talk to someone – as a primary part of their treatment, regardless of the diagnosis they have received, and regardless of their ethnic origin (or any other factor that is irrelevant to the need for someone to talk to)

- people who have experienced sexual abuse as a child be provided with the opportunity to have appropriate psychotherapy or counselling at a time when they are ready for it

- psychiatrists, GPs, CPNs, keyworkers and care managers ensure that people who are referred for psychotherapy or counselling are given clear information (both verbal and written) about the form of treatment, and what they might expect from it

- information provided to people includes what to do if they are not happy with the therapist or counsellor (eg a list of alternatives) or if they are not satisfied with what is happening in the therapy

- training bodies for counselling, psychotherapy and clinical psychology and others providing 'talking treatments' review their training courses to ensure that they recognise formally the views and experiences of service users

- psychiatrists, GPs, CPNs, keyworkers and care managers undertake regular reviews of treatment, in order to ensure that people are happy with the form of therapy or counselling they are receiving and the person they are receiving it from

- research organisations and funders prioritise further research in participation with service users, in order to understand what it is that people find helpful about talking treatments, and for what problems and in what circumstances they are most helpful

- research organisations and research funders take into account the human relations elements of counselling and psychotherapy (to include user defined outcomes), in order to make more realistic assessments of effectiveness.

COMPLEMENTARY THERAPIES

INTRODUCTION

This section covers the range of complementary therapies experienced by the people we interviewed, and explores the ways in which they were found to be helpful. Some approaches, like relaxation techniques, are not always thought of as therapies, but as they were used therapeutically by some people, classifying them as complementary therapies is a useful collective shorthand.

Complementary therapies have become increasingly popular in recent years, and studies have shown that they are beginning to become more easily available on the NHS – predominantly in the treatments of drug and alcohol abuse, HIV and Aids, and some other physical conditions. They are more rarely given or considered in relation to mental health services, although this too is beginning to change; due to the increased interest in this area, the Mental Health Foundation published a comprehensive review of research into complementary therapies in mental health in 1998.[9] In *Knowing our own Minds*,[10] complementary therapies constituted one of the main themes under investigation, alongside other alternative approaches. We categorised them under headings of: art/creative therapies, physical (touch) therapies, exercise/postural therapies, and dietary/herbal therapies. The most commonly experienced of these were the art and creative therapies, perhaps more often provided through statutory and voluntary sector day services than others. However, all of the complementary therapies were very popular, and many people in the survey expressed the wish to gain access to more of them.

In this study, although relatively few people had used complementary therapies, we were able to explore in more depth the ways in which they had found them helpful or therapeutic. Table 7 lists the different therapies people had tried. There were no particular groups within our sample, whether by personal characteristics or experience or by geographical area, who had particular experience of using complementary therapies. Rather, the dominant factor appeared to be easy access to therapies through local services or contacts.

Table 7: Complementary therapies used
• Reflexology
• Healing and Reiki
• Relaxation
• Meditation
• Yoga
• Tai Chi
• Homeopathy
• Herbal remedies
• Acupuncture
• Aromatherapy and massage
• Aromatherapy oils at home (bath or burner)

WHY DID PEOPLE USE COMPLEMENTARY THERAPIES?

Overall, people's comments suggest that they saw complementary therapies as distinctly complementary to conventional approaches rather than as a substitute. In this sense they were truly complementary rather than alternative therapies. Indeed, some mental health professionals recommended that people try these approaches in addition to medication or talking therapies. This woman, who was going to see a herbalist, is typical:

'I am hoping she will give me something, she won't be able to substitute my medication, although it would be great if she could, but something that works alongside the medication and improves my life a bit more, then I am willing to do it.'

Very many people hoped complementary therapies would help them relax, recognising that relaxation was good for their mental health. Obviously this was the reason people tried relaxation classes, but also why they had massage or reflexology and tried more active therapies like yoga and Tai Chi. The few people who saw a healer did not, apparently, expect to be 'cured', but rather to feel calmer and more at ease with themselves.

Some of the support groups and day centres that people attended offered relaxation classes and other therapies, such as massage or reflexology, free of charge, although often on a short term basis; it seemed that some people had tried them because of this ready accessibility. A few people paid for massage, aromatherapy or to see a herbalist; these people were convinced of the benefits of their chosen approach. A relatively small number of people had tried several different complementary therapies; it seemed that once someone had tried one, they were more likely to try another. Perhaps this suggests that there are some people who are generally open-minded about, or convinced of, the potential benefits of complementary therapies, whereas those who are more sceptical are less likely to try them in the first place.

CHOICE OF COMPLEMENTARY THERAPY

As suggested above, people were more likely to use complementary therapies because they wanted to, rather than because they had been prescribed to them; in other words, there was a more active choice involved (as long as money was not an issue). Determining which therapies were most beneficial depended on individual factors: therapies that some people found very helpful were described by others as not at all helpful and even potentially frightening. Most people had a prior idea about what they would find helpful and so hadn't tried things that they were sceptical about. However, some people had been surprised when a therapy they thought would be relaxing had brought uncomfortable issues to the fore. For instance, although the majority of people enjoyed massage, some women who had been sexually abused found the level of physical intimacy difficult:

'I did find that I just could never relax with, like aromatherapy, and I just couldn't. If I tried to mention my history, I'd get to a certain point and then it just all comes crashing back.'

People's attitude towards complementary therapy overall, or to particular therapies, influenced whether or not they found it helpful. One woman pointed out that sometimes it can be difficult to get into a frame of mind which would give a therapy a chance to work. She was talking here about relaxation:

'... one of the things that I have always found rather contradictory is that people with anxiety and depression are told to relax and listen to relaxation tapes and it is one of the most difficult things to try and make yourself do when you are actually tensed up. I found that I could do it sometimes, but it had to only be at a certain time and I was better actually trying not to relax, and doing something while I calmed down a bit, and then try and relax when I was on a more even keel, because to try and relax when you were... is just counter-productive to me, it made me worse.'

It might be that a different approach, such as massage, would have helped these people to unwind sufficiently to then be able to practice relaxation techniques themselves. One woman said that she was only able to benefit from relaxation classes once she was on medication which allowed her to start to unwind, again showing how the two approaches can complement each other:

'I went there for relaxation every week or every day I suppose for seven years... I found it really helpful once I was on the medication and my body was settling down and stayed down and my thoughts went elsewhere – I found that really helpful.'

However, one person found that medication interfered with her ability to use meditation as an aid to relaxation. These examples show how difficult it is to generalise about approaches which require active engagement on the part of the person trying them, yet most people felt that a positive attitude was necessary if they were to benefit from complementary therapies:

'I think you have got to have your mind in focus usually for complementary therapies. I don't think you can just go and say it will work for me, I think you have got to apply some thinking – like I am sure it is going to work.'

It follows that if it is necessary to feel positive or at least open-minded about complementary therapies, people should be able to choose which approach they want to try. The importance of matching the therapy or technique to the individual is further illustrated by the following:

'... the one thing the psychologist did for me that was helpful, was taught me how to do deep breathing. To relax... It really works as well... It takes away the tightness in the chest and all that. [Whereas] I've been to meditation. I been there, didn't find that helpful. It really terrified me... Focusing on myself. I didn't want to do that.'

WHAT WAS HELPFUL ABOUT PARTICULAR THERAPIES?

In this section, we first look at what people had to say about individual groups of complementary therapies, and then draw out the common themes emerging across all of the therapies.

Massage, aromatherapy and reflexology

Many people found massage and reflexology very relaxing, either on their own or using aromatherapy oils. A very specific benefit was to help manage the side-effects of medication, by inducing physical relaxation:

'My medication stiffens up my muscles, and knots them all up, makes them all knotted and horrible, so the massage part of the aromatherapy treatment is absolutely wonderful to say the least. It just, you know, knocks about 20 years off me.'

Other people talked about the connection between physical and mental relaxation:

'[Massage] helped me a lot. An awful lot. [I felt] more relaxed. Like, there was tension... taken... being taken away from you, from your muscles. And all the strain in your muscles, tensions being taken away from your muscles. And it's like, when you exercise your muscles, that's what it's like. It's stress being taken away. It's a nice feeling.'

Massage and reflexology differ from other approaches in that they involve physical contact. Whereas for some people, as mentioned earlier, touch could be experienced as quite threatening or invasive, there were others who found this aspect of physical therapies especially beneficial:

'I guess because I don't have physical relationships with guys and I am not married yet... I find the sensation of touch very, very comforting and very relaxing... and because it touches certain parts of your body, and sort of, um, is connected to certain other muscles and stuff, I just find it very relaxing.'

'I need a massage, or I need some kind of physical, you know, contact with another human being, is the only thing that's going cure it, it's not going to be, you know, drugs or what have you.'

This woman went on to say that physical touch was also helpful because it would release things that she could not let go of through talking alone. For this reason, the counsellor she had found most useful was a woman who had occasionally used touch:

'... it released so much in my body, from what had happened in the past, and brought everything up to the surface, in a way that talking never had.'

Aromatherapy alone, without massage, could also be relaxing. Some people used aromatherapy oils at home, believing that their properties would be beneficial. They were used for relaxation or to influence mood; either by self-massage, burning the oils or putting them in the bath:

'I buy things that are for the nerves, you know, for my ailment... It wakes me up and makes me more alert, yes.'

Relaxation and meditation

Many people had been offered relaxation classes held at their support group or day centre. Some had used relaxation tapes at home, either on their own initiative or because they had been recommended by their keyworker or mental health care team. They described how relaxation techniques made them feel:

'Made me feel quite, um, I don't know a word for it, just relaxing really, and dreaming of stuff. I had some good dreams. If I can keep me eyes shut of course. Eh, that was quite good actually, I used to like relaxation.'

'I just felt rested and relaxed – thoughts were away somewhere else and you were able to get up from your relaxation and go to another group without having all these weird thoughts going round your head or really feeling anxious, you just went and did it, instead of before it would be 'oh no I am not going' – you would just sit and do nothing. I found it really helpful – relaxation.'

A few people found meditation helpful. One woman had begun meditating as a result of reading the Bible and found that it helped to clear her head; one man combined relaxation and meditation:

'... when I relax I just don't think about anything – I just give my mind a rest and give my back a rest at the same time, and usually while I am relaxing I drift into meditating and I am thinking about ways I can improve my situation, like when I started meditating about work and getting back to work, I was thinking of ways I can do that myself rather than depending on somebody else to do it for me.'

Yoga and Tai Chi
Yoga was another therapy that people found helped them to relax. One woman preferred it to relaxation classes:

'Yoga was good. I found that helpful. I don't like relaxation. I found if I lie on the floor and try to relax, I immediately tense up and that always makes me worse. [Yoga was] relaxing and calming... it helps your concentration.'

Yoga and Tai Chi use a series of movements and postures to focus awareness and develop physical and mental strength. These people were in no doubt that they were helpful.

'I had a breath problem as well, I couldn't breathe properly... He [doctor] sent me to yoga classes and that was good. Physically and mentally it's good. I'm OK now, I breathe now, I'm OK now. [It helped with] breathing, physical exercise and mentally relaxing.'

'... it was something relaxing, you could focus your mind and lose all the stresses and strains from wearing yourself out... You're exercising and you're relaxing at the same time... You're concentrating and relaxing on something and nothing. Whenever I concentrate on something I feel better.'

'[Tai Chi] was so – it was relaxing and somehow cleared your mind. You had to concentrate so much on learning the movements that whether it was the process of concentrating to learn the movements that took your mind off your problems, or whether it was the actual doing of the movements that made you feel better – but it really did have a positive effect.'

Most forms of Yoga and Tai Chi involve elements of meditation practice, or induce a similar state of mind:

'Meditation I've found useful... I find it helps me to be aware of the moment rather than, you know, worrying about what's going to happen next week or something... I think meditation's very useful. Tai Chi also, I've tried that... that's the same thing, I mean it's a bit like moving meditation really.'

Other therapies

A few people had seen a herbalist or used herbal remedies. One woman had been prescribed camomile tea from a herbalist, which helped her to sleep:

'I used to wake up a lot and have broken sleep and wake up a lot in the night, and walk around. Now it has sort of got me a little bit more rested, I do wake up but I don't walk about, I am a bit more relaxed and lie in bed until I fall asleep again.'

A small number of people had seen healers. One of these, an African-Caribbean man, spoke about his experiences at length. He had seen three different healers: two who practised forms of hands-on healing and one who did Reiki. He described how healing had helped overall:

'[They] actually helped me work out a load of baggage, and get rid of a load of stuff that wasn't there, that, that was there, and shouldn't have been... I think it helped me at the time to, how can I say, um, it helped me to sort of, I think, be a freer person in my mind, um, I think it helped me to be, helped me to be more together with myself inside, but I think, um, it was beneficial, it was beneficial... I felt at one with myself, I felt peaceful with myself.'

He talked at length about what was helpful about seeing a particular healer, who was:

'A black, black guy, very nice person, understood where I was coming from, and understood what was happening in my mind... he was working with guides that had been... channelled through him. And this was, er, quite productive, very helpful... it seemed to reconnect me back to how I wanted to be with myself, and the person that I was trying to be before I saw all of these healers before. It seemed, he seemed to sort of like, clear out a lot of the crap that was going on in my mind. And, sort of like, help me to get back to being together with myself. Um, he was a very nice person and quite understanding, quite compassionate as well.'

He explained that he did not think it was because he was black that he had been more helpful than the other healers he had seen:

'I wasn't looking at it in terms of colour... I think it was just a different way of understanding, he was much more compassionate, and much more caring, and much more gentle... I think the most helpful thing that I've had is going to see this black healer. And that's been the most helpful.'

The black healer listened to his story without judging him and showed compassion, qualities we have seen emerge as valued within other relationships (see Chapter 2 and the sections on *Talking therapies* and *Mental health professionals* in this chapter).

COMMON THEMES ACROSS THERAPIES

A number of strong common themes emerge from this exploration, which demonstrate that complementary therapies do tend to provide similar benefits to people but that individual factors about both person and therapy will affect the choice of therapy. Equally there were a small number of people who are more likely to try many different complementary therapies because they perceive the general approach to be a natural alternative for them.

Common themes

- Relaxation
- Concentration/focusing the mind
- Help with sleep
- Peace
- Taking control
- Compassion, caring
- Time to talk

Of these, by far the strongest theme was relaxation. As we have seen (above) many people spoke of the value of achieving a state of relaxation through sometimes different routes. Similarly, relaxation emerges as an important theme from Chapter 4, where a range of different personal strategies are considered. This woman explains the value of relaxation:

'I only had neck massage and the hands. I found that really comforting and warm and I almost fell asleep with that as well, and I felt really relaxed – having been all tensed up and frightened, it was like, 'oh, I feel great' and off I went.'

Another important theme to emerge was the role that complementary therapies could play in enabling someone to take some kind of action in alleviating their own symptoms or distress. This could be an important contribution towards beginning the process of taking control over distress or self-management:

'I'm pretty certain that there is something to do with, I don't know, a biochemical or pharmacological effect. But also, I do think there is an effect in like, actually taking, beginning to take action again. And actually taking control. I mean, I'm sure that there'd be some effect if I was given a smartie and told it was a homeopathic remedy. Just taking it would have some effect. Because again, I'd feel like, yes, I've taken some action about it.'

The third major theme concerned the role of the therapists themselves, and as we have seen elsewhere, this could be vital in enabling the person to feel relaxed and accepted within the therapy. People valued the fact that complementary therapists were calm and non-judgmental and gave them sufficient time to express themselves and relax. Their experience of using complementary therapies often contrasted sharply with conventional medicine, which was characterised by a long wait for a hurried consultation. In other words, those aspects that were peripheral to the action of the therapy itself, were therapeutic because they fostered people's self-esteem and potential for healing.

COMPLEMENTARY THERAPIES AS 'MOST HELPFUL' STRATEGY

Only two people named complementary therapies amongst the 'most helpful' strategies or supports they had encountered. One of these was the African-Caribbean man mentioned above, whose experience of the black healer was so compassionate and healing. The other was a man who combined homeopathy with counselling for his 'winning formula'. This man had lived in a town where all the doctors in the NHS general practice used homeopathy as well as conventional medication, and although he had now moved, he continued to see a homeopath as well as having counselling. He had subsequently come to accept it as an important part of his treatment, demonstrating the mediating influence of accessibility on the use of complementary therapies.

ACCESS AND CHOICE

Many of the people who took part in the study were able to get these therapies free of charge from the day centres/user groups they attended. However, some had to pay for them and this meant that they could not have treatments as often as they would have liked. As these women said:

'I really think it would be something brilliant to put on the NHS. If I could choose anything, I wouldn't choose any drug, I'd choose that.'

'I used to go to… a mental health users group and it was run by two females and they had lots of things going on – aromatherapy, reflexology – just different things… and I found the reflexology really wonderful and the massage, and that really helped a lot, you felt so relaxed, it was lovely. But there is not a lot of it going round, that is one problem, and obviously I think it would be great if they had it in doctors' surgeries, so that you could use it as a service on the National Health Service, because it did me a lot of good.'

As with talking therapies, access and choice affect people's ability to experience and to benefit from complementary therapies. From the interviews, it is clear that whilst many people had found complementary therapies very helpful, they had rarely continued with them for long periods, or had tended to drop in and out of them. Closer examination reveals that local services may have made certain therapies available to service users for periods of time, but were rarely able to do so on a long term basis. Consequently people's ability to use these therapies as a long term strategy is inevitably limited by cost and availability.

A number of people, including a couple of Asian women attending a voluntary sector project, had experience of receiving a combination of counselling and a physical therapy, such as aromatherapy massage or reflexology. They were very appreciative of the effects that this combination could achieve for them, feeling that the two approaches treated things in different ways and so increased the relative benefits:

'It was almost like having a lot of the stress massaged out of your body; so having released it orally and having expressed it, it was physically removed and it felt as though – I was just completely lighter all over, and very, very relaxed.'

RECOMMENDATIONS: COMPLEMENTARY THERAPIES

The main difficulty with complementary therapies is the failure of medical practitioners and mental health workers to take their potential benefits seriously. There are many chronic physical conditions which are seen to benefit from complementary medicine within a self-management approach, and mental ill-health should be seen in a similar way. Any approach that can foster healing, relaxation and positive self-management should be supported and promoted within a mental health setting.

We recommend that
- **comissioners and purchasers of services, including Primary Care Groups, encourage the provision of complementary therapies within mental health services**
- **all mental health workers ensure that people are given information about complementary therapies/therapists available through their local services, and promote individual choice of therapies and treatments**
- **professional and training bodies for complementary therapies make available information about the potential benefits of their therapies for people with mental health problems, and how best to access them**
- **research organisations and funders prioritise further research in partnership with service users, in order to find out more about the ways in which different forms of therapy are helpful to people with mental health problems**
- **mental health service providers ensure that they are making a choice of therapies and treatments available to their service users, including complementary therapies (see note below).**

Note: The Patients' Charter states: 'You have the right to have an explanation of any proposed treatment, including any risks involved in that treatment and any alternatives, before you decide whether to agree with it... You can expect to be told what treatments are available other than medications.'

1   Mind (1996) *Mind's Yellow Card Scheme Reporting the Adverse Effects of Psychiatric Drugs: First Report.* London Mind Publications
    Mind (1998) *Psychiatric drugs: users' experiences and current policy and practice* London: Mind Publications
2   Rogers, A Pilgrim, D & Lacey, R (1992) *Experiencing Psychiatry: users' views of services* London: Mind Publications
3   Chapter 2 in Faulkner, A (1997) *Knowing our own Minds* London: The Mental Health Foundation
4   See, for example, Rogers, A Pilgrim, D and Lacey, R (1993) *Experiencing Psychiatry: users' views of services* London: Mind
    Publications; and Chapter 4 in: Faulkner, A (1997) *Knowing our own Minds* The Mental Health Foundation, London
5   NHS Executive (1996). NHS *Psychotherapy Services in England: review of strategic policy* Department of Health, London
6   See also: Yazdani, A (1998) *Young Asian Women and Self-Harm* Newham Innercity Multifund and Newham Asian Women's Project,
    London
7   Frederick, J (1991) *Positive Thinking for Mental Health* The Black Mental Health Group, London
8   See Fernando, S (1991) *Mental Health, Race and Culture* Macmillan/Mind Publications, London. Also: The Mental Health Foundation
    (1995) *Mental Health in Black and Minority Ethnic People: the Fundamental Facts* The Mental Health Foundation, London
9   Wallcraft, J (1998) *Healing Minds* Mental Health Foundation, London
10 Chapter 3 in Faulkner, A (1997) *Knowing our own Minds* Mental Health Foundation, London

4   Personal and self-help strategies

INTRODUCTION

This chapter addresses the sources of support developed by people through personal and self-help strategies. It is not comprehensive in its coverage of the strategies mentioned, but covers the main themes discussed by the people we interviewed: sport and physical exercise, creative expression, religious and spiritual beliefs. Many of the strategies and supports mentioned elsewhere in this report could have been developed through 'personal self-help strategies' – in particular, those involving the support of other people. However, what distinguishes the strategies included in this chapter is the importance placed by people on finding sources of support or help through their own resources, beliefs or lifestyle choices. The principles of individual choice and self-determination are central to an understanding of what helps people to cope and to live with mental distress. As we previously quoted in _Knowing our own Minds_:

'Many of us believe that empowerment and control over our lives is essential to emotional healing...'

'To regain control over our lives we need to be active, assertive and strong. Our concern is that, all too often, treatments encourage inactivity, passivity and compliance.'

Read and Wallcraft, 1992[1]

A theme underlying the strategies in this chapter is that many people talked of finding ways of taking control of the distress internally through mental or emotional attitudes or approaches. These approaches had often been developed originally through external sources of help and support, but had since become internalised or 'owned' by people as they developed self-reliance or control over their distress. Some of the people for whom these approaches were particularly important were people who either could not, or chose not to, depend upon others for their support. Perhaps what is most interesting about these strategies is how people discovered or learnt about them.

These approaches largely fall into two categories. One has, at its heart, the value of achieving peace of mind; people who talked about this had found ways of achieving peace or quiet within themselves, enabling them to live with their difficulties or to prevent further pressure or stress from affecting them within. For other people, their personal approach had a more proactive connotation, although it still frequently involved the encouragement or development of a mental or emotional state within oneself, a positive frame of mind or self-affirmation to overcome negative thoughts or feelings.

POSITIVE SELF-HELP APPROACHES

Many people described ways in which they had developed positive mental or emotional self-help strategies to overcome negative thoughts or feelings, or specific symptoms. For some people, these strategies had a proactive element to them, perhaps developed originally through therapy or in conversation with others, whereas for others they originated from within a fundamental belief in self-reliance. As one person put it:

'You've got to do a certain amount for yourself, you know, nobody else is going to do it for you.'

Self-reliance, a fundamental belief in oneself as the primary source of help, a sense of responsibility for oneself, all seemed to have developed out of fairly long-term experience – of both mental distress and of a range of different services and supports:

'I believe in taking responsibility for my own life... I just believe in myself, myself is what gets me through things, and plus my extended family which are my friends.'

'Mainly the anger, getting angry with the illness, that would be top of the list really, over the days saying 'I've had enough'... you just have to learn strategies to deal with that, so I found the anger one is the best.'

There were also some specific resources, which had paved the way for people to develop these strategies. For a couple of people, a form of counselling or psychotherapy had enabled them to develop strategies or a positive approach towards their distress, an approach that had come to transcend the original therapy:

'Now, after a period of time in cognitive therapy, I think it is quite logical and it sounds quite reasonable, you know, and now I can see it in personal terms, I can see how my emotions are very much affected, have been very much affected by my perceptions, and perceptions of what other people think of me, and attitudes to me, being a person emotionally, it has, I believe it has a very positive side, the positive side being me...'

One or two people had developed their strategies through finding out information from others or through reading books about their illness or about self-help strategies. One woman had begun to read self-help books alongside finding assistance from her GP:

'I began to be able to take a little bit of initiative in helping myself. Doing things to help my depression rather than just swallowing pills, because up until then, I felt the actual day to day depression was not being addressed. And I found there were things I could do to stop my negative thoughts, being aware of my negative thoughts and try to turn them to more positive was a step I could take for myself. And I found the reading very helpful indeed.'

PEACE OF MIND

Many people spoke of the value of finding peace of mind or contentment within themselves, perhaps also highlighting the value of building and sustaining a safe space within themselves, strengthening an inner self-protection:

'I've found the art of contentment, and that's it. I don't want nobody to upset it. I say, just, I've found the art of contentment, I don't want, ask, for nothing...'

Some of the routes through which people had achieved this are discussed elsewhere in this chapter, and some in other chapters (see, for example, Chapter 2). Many people had found peace of mind through their religious or spiritual beliefs, a source of strength and comfort in times of distress. Some people's religious or spiritual beliefs had been the source of assistance they needed in developing positive strategies or self-affirmations for managing their distress. For one woman, the certain belief that God loved her and that therefore she was a good person, made her illness easier to bear:

'To know that I'm a good person and I try, and if the mental illness has come, then I'll just have to live with it, 'cause as long as I know I'm a good person... that makes me cope with my illness a lot better.'

Others had found peace of mind through the comfort and affirmation found in the company of others, a 'safe haven' in a storm. Some people had found a safe space in counselling or therapy, but many mentioned self-help groups or day centres as having been their route towards peace of mind. For example, one person described her strategy for overcoming a period of depression:

'Patience – knowing and trying to remind myself that the depression will lift and that I will enjoy things again. It is very difficult to remember that, it's very difficult to remember when I'm depressed that it is not going to last forever, that it's going to go. It has gone before and it will this time.'

Other activities also had the potential to instigate calm or peace for the person undertaking them. Creative activities and physical exercise are examples of this, but one other mentioned in this context is gardening:

'When you're doing something like that your mind is quite calm and it calms the mind, it's a bit like, it's taking space out, um, you don't have to think of anything... the nearest thing is some people who have different religions can actually sort of space themselves away from their problems by thinking of something else.'

MANAGING DISTRESS AND NEGOTIATING PEACE

We have written elsewhere of the value of finding acceptance, both of oneself and of the illness or distress that one is struggling with. It seems that what many people are talking about here, is reaching a state of 'equilibrium' or peace with their distress, through whatever route they have taken to get there. Some degree of negotiation has taken place along the way, which has enabled people to accommodate their distress or find a place for it within their lives through taking more active control. There is almost a sense of reaching a truce underlying many people's words, as they describe the positive strategies or approaches they have developed. As one person put it:

'Having to acknowledge that I've got that, a mental illness, has been a struggle for me, but I've got to the point now where I'm happy and I'm proud of it. You know, I don't care what other people say about mental illnesses. I know the truth.'

SPORT AND PHYSICAL EXERCISE

We know from *Knowing our own Minds* that various forms of sport and physical exercise can be important to many people with mental health problems. Physical exercise, or at least aerobic exercise, can lead to biochemical changes in the body that can lead to improvements in psychological well-being. A review of research into exercise and mental health (Glenister, 1996[a]) suggested that regular aerobic exercise can bring about a reduction in depression, as measured on standard depression scales. However, most research studies have been conducted on 'healthy populations' and tend to show positive improvements in psychological health and stress reduction. Interestingly, the review also suggested that exercise is not enough in itself to improve depression and anxiety, but that a personal or subjective perception of improvement is important as well.

In the *Knowing our own Minds* survey, we looked at physical activities in two different ways: 'exercise and postural therapies' such as yoga and Alexander technique, and other sporting activities under the general heading of 'hobbies and leisure activities'. In the first category, 31% of the sample, or 122 people, had some experience of an exercise or postural therapy, and the majority of these had found them helpful. In addition, sport and physical exercise formed the most common type of hobby and leisure activity mentioned, with 95 people recording some active participation and 47 people mentioning walking as a helpful regular activity.

In this study many people reported that a form of sport or physical exercise was a valuable activity in their lives. People mentioned a wide variety of different activities, including walking, swimming, running, gym, cycling, dancing, badminton, tennis, climbing, gardening, and hard physical work. The important questions for us to understand here are: why and in what ways did people find physical activity helpful to them, and how might a sport or physical activity help with or alleviate mental distress?

Common themes
- Physical health and weight control
- Mental health and well-being
- Relaxing, stress relieving
- Distraction... from hearing voices
- Getting out of the house
- 'Fitting in'

Many people talked about 'feeling better' or 'feeling good' as a result of physical exercise, although this clearly meant different things to different people. The themes and issues that arose are actually quite complex, in some cases influenced by people's sense of knowing that exercise might be 'good for you' but not always being able to act on that knowledge. Thus, whilst many people talked about the health aspects of physical exercise, some expressed them in more theoretical terms than others, whose direct experience of the benefits caused them to believe more strongly in the health benefits of physical exercise. Other themes mentioned in relation to sport and physical exercise were: stress relief, weight control or weight loss, mental distraction, the opportunity to get out of the house, and calming or relaxing effects. Some specific strategies in relation to hearing voices were mentioned as well.

PHYSICAL HEALTH

As mentioned above, the relation between physical exercise, physical health and mental well-being was a fairly complex area. For some people, the 'feel good' factor associated with physical exercise seemed to be based on what they believed about it rather than on how they felt as a result of it. In this sense it was linked in their minds with physical health or fitness rather than with mental health or well-being, and often linked also with other health-related behaviours:

'Jogging, it makes me feel a lot better if I do it, because I... thinking to myself, yeah, I'm trying to keep myself fit.'

'It makes me wanna stop smoking because I feel, when I'm training, I feel faint, and I says, if I didn't smoke, I'd be even more fitter.'

The knowledge or awareness of the potential of physical exercise to provide health benefits did not necessarily translate into action; for some people this awareness was insufficient motivation for them to actively participate – and indeed it could be the source of guilt or sense of failure:

'The one strategy I feel I need to do is, to do some exercise, and I've been saying that now for over a year. But, I can't get round to doing it... to make me feel a lot better... So I think, if you're working out, you going to feel better, you're obviously going to be healthier, and I need to lose my weight fast.'

This person had been recommended to take exercise by her psychiatrist, but had not yet managed to follow it up despite previous experience in the past of enjoying dancing.

Weight control

Several people talked about physical exercise in the context of managing their weight, which for some was crucial to improving their self-image and self-esteem, as well as having health benefits. Weight gain is a common side-effect of certain psychiatric drugs, and this was an issue of great concern to some people:

'I feel that I'm actually trying to do something about the amount of weight I gained at one stage. I still need to lose, um, about 3 or 4 stone, but I know I was about 3 or 4 stone heavier than I am now when I started using the gym a year ago... And because it has a health benefit, it has a mental health benefit, because, um, I'm a believer in the two being tied together.'

MENTAL HEALTH AND WELL-BEING

There were many people in the study who identified the potential for physical exercise to create a tangible 'feel good' factor, particularly as an after-effect of the exercise, as the main benefit they experienced from physical exercise. People talked about feeling better afterwards, feeling 'brilliant' or high, and some described a reduction in their depression:

'I kind of think it does have a big effect on your mental health. It makes, it's not necessarily the actual, it's how you feel afterwards, yeah. You know, you go for a swim and you feel brilliant afterwards... And if it's, just that change of mood, then you're, like, saying, 'oh well, I want to go out tonight' and then you're off again, you're into the routine or something again.'

Several people talked more specifically about the ability of physical exercise to lift depression, although as we shall see later on, this could be variable for some people, since depression can also cause reduced motivation and lethargy making activity of any kind difficult to initiate:

'It's almost like getting your anger out of yourself for all the things that you've been through, and getting your anger out which makes you, I think it makes your depression less a little bit.'

The person above was also aware of the temporary nature of the effect, going on to say:

'When you climb, or when you play badminton, and when you finish playing it, the depression, you don't get so depressed for a few hours afterwards, but then your depression you know, creeps back in again.'

RELAXING, STRESS RELIEVING

One way in which physical exercise can enable someone to 'feel better' is by providing an outlet or release for stress and producing a calming or relaxing effect. This was a common theme amongst the people who valued the contribution of physical exercise to their lives. From *Knowing our own Minds* we know that many people valued relaxation, whatever the nature of their mental health problems or distress. There is no doubt that it is a ubiquitous issue, valued across different therapies and activities as well as across different people and problems:

'I can jump on my bike if I want to, get there, come back, and it relieves a lot of stress, you know, it does relieve a lot of stress riding my bike, and it makes me feel great you know, I wouldn't like anybody to nick it!'

'When you're actually doing something physically, your mind is calmed in that way.'

One or two people mentioned the ability of physical exercise to calm the mind when they were feeling high or manic. One person, for example, found gardening helpful in this respect, and others found walking to have a calming effect. This was complex, however, as it did not work like that for everyone; there were people who found physical exercise to be unhelpful and exhausting when experiencing a 'high' or manic episode.

DISTRACTION

Like relaxation, the ability to find some form of distraction from distress, thoughts or feelings, is valued by many people, and is named as a benefit of a number of different activities, including creative activities, and various hobbies and leisure activities. People talked of sport or physical exercise being able to distract through the active participation in something physical, sometimes enabling the focus of attention to be on the activity of the body in preference to the mind or emotions. This is not to suggest that the mind and body are separate entities, but that the focus of attention can be moved between them to the benefit of the individual:

'It's like you're forcing all your energy into concentrating to holding onto these rocks, 'cause if, say, you're 100 feet up, you can't make mistakes, so you have to concentrate very, you know, very hard... I think it takes your mind off the depression, because you're concentrating on keeping yourself alive and not falling down, and that takes a lot of you away.'

'... once I do get there and once I do go through the workout, it completely focuses my mind, like whereas I may have been stressed about something, I start thinking about other things or I will sort of work myself through it, as I run or workout or whatever, and it just seems less significant usually.'

...from hearing voices

A particular version of distraction mentioned by a few people, was the ability to use involvement in a sport or physical exercise to distract the mind from hearing their internal voices:

'Because some of the exercises are repetitive they take over from the repetitive nature of the voices. And, you know, I can, if I'm say, rowing, I can count the number of strokes rather than listen to the voices saying 'Dead, dead, dead, dead, dead!'

'When I was swimming, the voices in my head, they don't do sort of swimming, and I say to my world, 'I am swimming for my own health, shut up!' They are disturbing the peace and I am doing back swimming.'

GETTING OUT OF THE HOUSE

Several people described the importance of being motivated to get up and out of the house, in order to walk or take part in another physical activity. Running and walking were typical of the activities valued in this respect:

'Just being out and away from everything. I like climbing up high so I can stand and look over the countryside. The freedom, it's lovely, makes me good, gives me a good feeling... Walking, even if I'm feeling really bad, really depressed, walking I can do, even if it is just round the park.'

'FITTING IN'

A number of people talked of the importance of being able to 'fit in', or to look or appear 'normal'. This is another issue that arises elsewhere in this report; taking part in the everyday activities that people who are assumed to be without mental health problems might take part in, is valued highly by some people. One person talked of this in relation to losing weight and appearing physically normal, but for others it was an aspect of the activity itself that enabled them to feel as if they were indistinguishable from the general population, or were seen to be returning to normal life:

'The role of swimming is that I can jump in a pool and nobody knows me and I am just another swimmer.'

'I keep thinking that the more normal you are, the happier you are, and the more there's nothing wrong with you... If you go into town and you look normal, that's a... that could be some sort of start.'

INDIVIDUAL ISSUES

There were one or two other specific strategies mentioned in relation to a physical activity that deserve a mention. One woman had, in the past, engaged in martial arts in order to manage her difficulties with touch and physical intimacy with other people:

'I'm more relaxed about people touching me now than I was, but in the time when I was absolutely frightened of people, I had physical closeness with people through martial arts, and quite intimate physical contact. And yet I couldn't handle it in a social situation. But with the boundaries of sport it was safe... Yeah, there was no ambiguity. The reasons for the physical contact were clear.'

MOTIVATION AND CHANGE

Active participation in a sport or physical activity requires a certain amount of motivation, both to initiate in the first place and then to take part in on a regular basis, particularly for people who felt obliged to do physical exercise for their health. People who could appreciate the benefits quite easily, or for whom the physical exercise had become a regular part of their lives, perhaps required less motivation than those who were still having to convince themselves of the known benefits. However, even those who did appreciate the benefits were, on occasions, unable to motivate themselves to do anything. This was sometimes due to periods of depression, but also to other variations in mood or in the nature of distress.

One woman said that she could only go to the gym or the swimming pool when she had sufficient energy, which was when she was high, but not when depressed:

'When I'm low, I'm feeling like someone's sitting on my chest and I can't breathe and I feel terrible, there's no way I could just go for a walk even.'

'When I am unhealthy or haven't been training or haven't worked out, I just feel the whole world is going to get on top of me, like my family, and then if I am not fit, I lack confidence and then I start to go mad and get lazy and lack motivation, and so generally 90 per cent of the time I keep myself fairly fit, do different things.'

One woman eloquently expressed the downside of physical exercise, the guilt or sense of failure from being unable to do something you know at some level should be good for you or might have quite specific health benefits. She did express pleasure in relation to walking the dog and gardening, but felt she should be doing something more:

'Yes, well I try and lead a healthy life, but it doesn't work, I am a miserable failure at it, you know, I am always trying to lose weight, increase my physical activity and everything else, but...'

SPORT AND PHYSICAL EXERCISE AS 'MOST HELPFUL' STRATEGY

We finish this section by returning to two people who had found physical exercise to be one of the most helpful elements in their overall strategy, and exploring with them why exercise was so important to them.

The first is a young woman with a diagnosis of schizophrenia. She had gained a lot of weight as a result of the medication she was taking, and found that exercise was an important part of managing her weight, particularly as she had in the past experienced eating disorders. But it had many other valuable contributions to make to her life as well; it was she who had found the repetitive nature of exercises in the gym to be helpful in countering the voices she was hearing. Exercise also helped improve her self-esteem and helped her sleep:

'I find it helps my self-esteem as well, which I redirect to affect upon my mental health problems... and because it has a health benefit, it has a mental health benefit. Because, um, I'm a great believer in the two being tied together.'

This woman had nominated three factors as equally important to her overall strategy: physical exercise, medication and community care, in the person of her CPN.

The second was also a woman with a diagnosis of schizo-affective disorder and depression. She had been actively involved in sport as a child and stopped running at the age of 13 when diagnosed with diabetes. However, she had subsequently stopped and started taking exercise at different times in her life, and at the time of the interview, felt she could attribute her current well-being to sport. She was now running competitively, swimming, cycling and walking:

'Basically someone said to me 'for God's sake get a grip, do something because no-one else can change your life but you' – so I joined a running group and things have just gone from bad to brilliant now – it has helped me a lot, so much so that I am now off my anti-depressants...'

'I try to keep active and go out as much as possible just to do something and that also keeps my mental health and my mental state better... I can definitely attribute my well-being to sport.'

'Sport does help, you know, if you are feeling a bit off, it helps your mental well-being also, so you know it would be nice, I think, because I have found that definitely for myself, to reach that to other people that it does, and can work.'

CREATIVE EXPRESSION

Access to art and creative activities is quite often facilitated through mental health day centres and projects in the voluntary or statutory sector, as well as through occupational therapy or other departments within psychiatric hospitals. In *Knowing our own Minds*, 45% of the people responding to the survey had some experience of art and creative therapies; although a larger number had taken part in non-therapeutic creative activities. The factors people mentioned in the survey as having been helpful were: the ability to express feelings, to focus or distract the mind, relaxation and social support.

In this study, we were able to understand these issues in more depth. A substantial number of people identified creative activities as being helpful to them in some way. There was no particular pattern to the people who valued creative activities in their lives; they came from a variety of backgrounds, experiences and personal characteristics. Although the activities mentioned were predominantly variations on art therapy, art groups, painting, and arts and crafts, people also mentioned ceramics and pottery, gardening, cooking, music, poetry and creative writing, and sewing or knitting.

Common themes
- Creating something
- Absorbing, distracting
- Expressing feelings
- Relaxing, calming
- 'Fitting in'
- Helpfulness of therapist/teacher

The themes that arose were similar to those in *Knowing our own Minds*, but the advantage of face-to-face interviewing is that it allows a more detailed understanding of the underlying issues.

CREATING SOMETHING

One of the core issues people talked about was the essence of creativity: what it meant to them to be creating a finished product, or what the process of being creative meant for them. Creating something could take place through a number of outlets: creating a poem, a painting, a garden or a meal. For some people the important issue was almost about daytime occupation, as an alternative to employment:

'How does it help? It's being creative. That is something else that you need to have in life, the ability to be creative, if you are unemployed.'

A sense of achievement, of pride in their creation was mentioned by several people in this context; the value of having created something from nothing, or of being able to 'leave your mark' in some way by creating something permanent:

'Well, whenever I am doing a piece of work or anything and I am receiving help to do it – having an interest with it, and if I can end up seeing the result and can say I have produced that – afterwards, it does give you a sense of achievement.'

Self-worth and self-esteem, which surely must be at the core of mental well-being, were touched on by some of those for whom the sense of achievement through creativity was valued particularly highly:

'Because to know that you've created something from nothing, you get a sense of achievement as well. That's that sense of achievement is, like, it's part of your self-worth.'

It is particularly notable that two people reported producing their best work, in this case poetry and creative writing, when in their worst periods of distress.

ABSORBING, DISTRACTING

For many people, creative activities offered them the opportunity to become absorbed in something that allowed them to forget their problems or to distract them from 'the everyday world', very much as identified in the 'Knowing our own Minds' survey. The activity, or the process of creating something, demands concentration and therefore necessitates a mental or emotional disengagement from your internal world. This may present only temporary relief, but is nevertheless a valued and pleasurable route through which to achieve this:

'Um, basically, the arts and crafts, I find, because I often think and concentrate on what I'm doing, so it means that I have to forget totally, you know, and concentrate on what I've got in front of me and what I'm doing.'

'Because I just concentrate on painting and draw home or flowers or something like that, and scenery, so I just occupy myself and I ignore some bad things when I'm drawing; afterwards it starts again sometimes, but it's a little bit of good. I think it's better when I do something.'

One woman described how crocheting could help her in both of the extremes of the mood swings she experienced, in different ways:

'It helps in different ways at different times; when I'm high it helps me to sit still, which I find very difficult because although I'm still my hands are moving, my brain's moving, but at least I'm not making myself tired... and sometimes, it can be a very undemanding thing to do when I'm low, that I don't have to leave the house to do.'

EXPRESSING FEELINGS

In contrast to the issue of distraction, some people valued creative activities for the opportunity they provided for the direct but non-verbal expression of feelings, or for giving physical form to overwhelming feelings or thoughts. This was particularly true of artistic activities, such as painting and drawing, but it also arose in relation to active participation in music. People spoke passionately of finding release for feelings that could be overwhelming and difficult to express in words. There seemed to be some consensus here that words were not always sufficient to give expression to such feelings, or perhaps were more difficult to access for some people. The process of giving expression to feelings in this way could be a release or relief, calming or 'therapeutic':

'The pictures are drawings of things which are in your mind, you know, things that you create, you know, when you're depressed and like, the drawings are what it's like to be very, very, very depressed, and do things when you feel a bit better, and so you can mix both of them together.'

Finding this non-verbal means of expression could be particularly important for people who found it difficult to expression themselves in words:

'Well, it made me put my worries down in the painting and that, things like that you know. And I can't read and write very well, I'm it's, what do you call that word, dyslexic.'

RELAXING, CALMING

A number of people described their creative activity as having a calming or relaxing effect on them. This was often associated with the expression of feelings (as mentioned above), but was also mentioned in connection with simple engagement in a non-verbal or physical activity:

'I find it calming... and, um, because I do all the academic stuff, it's nice to do something different than write... you use the potter's wheel and just relax, so it's very good.'

'FITTING IN'

As with sport and physical exercise, it was the assumed normality of the activity that was important to some people – offering, as it does, the opportunity to 'fit in' with other people, or to find acceptance in an environment where 'mental illness' is not a pre-requisite for participation (on adult education classes):

'Well, just having the opportunity in what is a good atmosphere without any fear of having a so-called illness, I can freely just go along to the class. There are able-bodied people there as well, just fit in, just like anybody else, you know.'

THE THERAPIST OR TEACHER

A couple of people spoke of the importance of their relationship with the art therapist or his/her ability to facilitate the benefits of the creative activity, whether it was about the opportunity to talk or aspects of the activity itself:

'It's the lady that does it, and, er, it is good to talk, because she lets me talk about what's in my head.'

'I enjoy doing things and do crafts and I enjoy making candles. And, I like the teacher, he's nice. There's no pressure on you to do anything.'

CREATIVITY AS 'MOST HELPFUL' ACTIVITY

We finish this section with a woman for whom art was a vital lifeline, and a fundamental coping strategy:

'The actual therapeutic effect of actually focusing all my tension on a painting, cleared all this crap from my head. And that's really powerful. Nothing else seems to do it for me... I need to do something that's totally absorbing, but that makes me focus on different issues. It's, it's just a creative distraction. It actually, the focusing the light or tone or colour, and what's happening on the paper or the canvas in front of me, actually blocks out the mental – you know, the 'what ifs'... and that anxiety, that perpetual conversation, it blocks it out. It goes, it disappears into the mist...

'The first time I found it helpful was working with that therapist I mentioned, that Gestalt one, because you know, she actually said to me, look, you're a creative person, you paint and draw, you're a designer, you know, have you never thought of actually trying to use that as a way of releasing some of your emotion. I can't remember whether she put it like that, but she said, you know, when you're, when you're in these rages... and I actually created an image of what that felt like. And that was really powerful for me. To actually manage to get it out of here and on to paper, it was very difficult doing it. I mean, I literally destroyed the image and re-created it, you know, that part of it, the fury was actually literally mashing up the paper and scribbling it, you know, and then putting it, repairing it, and putting it back together...

'Art, in a nutshell, art. It has kept me alive, I can't explain the number of times it's actually, actually saved my life. And the only reason I nearly got admitted this last time, was because I couldn't even, even get the ability to pick up my paints. And I thought I was on the way out. If I couldn't do that, I thought, I actually haven't got that lifeline. Because that's the one thing I've hung onto every time... No doubt whatsoever, no doubt. Best prescription: a set of paints, a few brushes and some space to paint in, works better than antidepressants any day.'

This woman was attending a voluntary sector arts project where space had been created for people to become involved in art or music or poetry, a space she found profoundly 'therapeutic' although it was not designated as a form of art therapy:

'It helps me see that somebody's actually bothering to provide a space where I and other people can be creative. It's that we matter. It's a very powerful message.'

RELIGIOUS AND SPIRITUAL BELIEFS

Since the publication of *Knowing our own Minds*, there have been a number of publications and conferences looking at the role of religious or spiritual beliefs in mental health, demonstrating a wider acknowledgement of their significance.[3,4] At the Mental Health Foundation we held a seminar for service users and survivors to come together and share their experiences and, out of that event, came our publication *The Courage to Bare our Souls*.[5] This was launched on 4th October 1999 alongside a report published by the Health Education Authority.[6]

The Institute of Psychiatry has held regular conferences on religion and mental health, and at the end of 1998 a consultation was convened at St George's House,

Windsor Castle, bringing together key academics, mental health professionals, service users, voluntary sector and religious professionals with an interest in religion and spirituality. A presentation from the *Strategies for Living* project again focussed on the views from service users and survivors, both positive and negative, and the spiritual needs these gave rise to.

Religion and spirituality is controversial and complex within mental health, and difficult for mental health services (and service users) to address. Whilst many people have found their beliefs supportive or even vital to their survival, others have found religious organisations or people within them to be intolerant or inflexible towards their distress. Still others who experience religious imagery within their voices or visual experiences, can find their religious beliefs very difficult to negotiate.

The findings of *Knowing our own Minds* began to unravel some of these different experiences. Just over 50% of the people in the survey (223) described religious or spiritual beliefs, and more than half of these (31% overall) espoused Christian beliefs. A higher proportion of African-Caribbean people in the study affirmed a religious (predominantly Christian) belief than of the white people or other minority ethnic groups.

Whilst many people mentioned the value of their beliefs or the support of their faith, there were also a significant number who talked of the potential for harm, sometimes talking of the difficulties surrounding guilt and sin, and sometimes of a failure on the part of religious communities to understand or address serious mental health problems. In this study we aimed to explore in more depth the helpful or supportive aspect of these beliefs, whilst in no way wishing to minimise the harm or the difficulties that people have experienced or continue to experience.

Many people talked about their religious or spiritual beliefs in these interviews. Again the majority talked about Christian beliefs, either directly or by implication. Some people had developed their own personal beliefs out of a belief in God, but alongside a rejection of conventional organised religion. These people were predominantly raised as Christians, abandoning this faith later in life. For some people this had a personal or a particular spiritual element, sometimes allied more with humanity or nature than with a belief in God.

There were several Moslems among the people we interviewed, one Sikh, one Jewish woman, one Spiritualist, and one Christian Scientist. There were also one or two people who described spiritual beliefs without mentioning a belief in God, either looking towards a belief in a 'higher power' or a sense within themselves of spiritual peace or meaning.

Across these different beliefs there were some powerful common themes running through people's explorations of how their beliefs sustained or supported them, with some variations as to the emphasis placed on them within the different faiths.

Common themes
- Meaning/purpose to life
- A reason for living
- Peace and comfort
- Prayer
- Inner spirituality
- Support of others
- The presence of God

MEANING/PURPOSE
Many people said that their beliefs gave them a sense of meaning or a purpose to their lives, a theme that crossed faith boundaries and applied equally to the non-religious spiritual beliefs as to the religious. For some people, this sense of meaning or purpose gave them something to hold on to, a belief to sustain them through periods of distress. At the core of this sustenance was the belief that, as one person described it, 'things happen for a purpose':

'There's a reason behind the paranoia and everything. I believe it is God, testing me, like.'

'The fact that I have been through all this is enabling me to live a better life and hopefully help others... I firmly believe that I am here to help others if I can. I haven't actually found out how yet, but that is part of my ongoing prayer – that God will show me what he wants me to do in that respect.'

Some people talked of something (or someone) higher, or more powerful than themselves, which enabled them to establish a sense of perspective or balance in their lives. A couple of people talked of this sense of meaning in their lives as creating 'a light at the end of the tunnel', or something to work towards, an afterlife that will give them peace:

'And I suppose because of my belief I know something better is in store. It is like, OK, this must be hell, but at the end of the journey I am going to be at peace anyway.'

REASON FOR LIVING

Several people talked of their faith giving them even more than meaning in their lives; it had given them a reason for remaining alive at times of despair when suicide might have been an option:

'That saves me every time you know. I think I would probably have done something to myself by now if I hadn't got my faith.'

PEACE AND COMFORT

Many people talked of the peace they discovered through their beliefs, whether from the faith itself or through associated activities such as prayer or reading the Bible or the Koran. As we have seen at the beginning of this chapter, peace of mind was highly valued as a state of mind or mental attitude with which to counter mental or emotional distress. Some people had found peace through other activities, whether physical or mental/emotional, but many had found it through religious or spiritual beliefs. Peace of mind was seen by many to be an important strategy for negotiating life with mental distress, and it is closely associated with acceptance which we have explored elsewhere. Several people talked specifically about how their religious or spiritual beliefs enabled them to live with their illness or distress – to find a means of accepting it and accepting themselves:

'Now I think, when I want to pray or when I read simple books about Islam and the spirit and essence of Islam, I find them very very peaceful and it doesn't matter what crazy world I am in at the time, with stress around me, I just feel very at peace...'

'If I'm in stress or crisis sometimes, one of the things I do is go to church, not to a service, but to be in the sanctuary of the church. The peace – just to be there in a peaceful, beautiful space that is huge and that is, sort of, the creation of human enterprise.'

PRAYER

Prayer was a highly valued activity by people with religious beliefs. Some people achieved peace of mind through prayer, whereas for others it became a means of 'offloading a burden' or of talking to someone who would listen to anything or everything without judgement. Prayer could be personal and private and need not be connected with religious observances or services; very often it was the personal nature of the activity that was of particular value, providing peace and comfort in distress.

INNER SPIRITUALITY

A number of people particularly valued an inner spirituality gained from their beliefs. In some ways similar in context to 'peace' or 'peace of mind', spirituality may be distinguished by its inner connectedness with something bigger or more powerful, whether thought of as God or as some more natural or human set of beliefs. One person, for example, spoke in very human terms of her understanding of spirituality:

'I often think about how my Gran brought up her children, how she lived her life, and she had a deep spiritual being, not necessarily formatted to a fixed religion – a spirituality within her. In her wisdom, she was very wise, very funny and her zest for life, I don't know, that sort of spiritual inner self, that deeper sort of thing, I think is important.'

'I just can forget about everything, and it's just like being close to nature and close to God or Goddess, or whatever label you want to stick on a greater spiritual being or whatever.'

Spirituality is a profoundly difficult concept to define, but a few of the people who spoke of its significance had a fairly clear idea of what it meant to them:

'Well I think being spiritual means that you sort of temper your actions towards other people, you care for other people, and you care for yourself, and you look after yourself.'

'My religious belief is that God is within yourself, there's nobody up in the sky looking on you. God is within yourself which is your spiritual within yourself, your honesty in everything. Now it's got to be taught to you from somewhere, but once it's within you, then you find it surrounds you.'

SUPPORT OF OTHERS

For some people, the most important element of their religious beliefs was the sense of belonging it gave them, to a group or community of people who they experienced as helpful and supportive. Some people spoke movingly of the support they had received in times of distress, whilst others simply of the social networks providing a lifeline and encouraging them out of the house and into company. One or two people valued this particularly because they belonged to an isolated minority religion, hence particularly valuing the company of others encountered at their place of worship:

'The only thing is that I use my religious place, the place of worship as a social place, because it is our own community, our own people believing the same book and the same leader, and you meet the people and you talk with them, rather than pray.'

For this person it is clear that sharing the same beliefs was important, although his emphasis was very much on the social aspect of meeting at the Mosque.

A few people had found a sense of true acceptance from the people they encountered through their place of worship: support and the ability to respond appropriately and flexibly during a crisis:

'It is acceptance as much as anything – never any problem about me being off with a mental illness.'

THE PRESENCE OF GOD

The sense of God's presence was a vital part of many people's religious and spiritual beliefs. His (or sometimes her) presence was sensed through a feeling of unconditional love, through prayer, or through the ability to heal. This sense of God's presence and the healing properties or reassurance it could give, was expressed more strongly by the Moslem people in the study than people with other faiths.

The feeling of being loved by God unconditionally – 'warts and all' – was an important aspect of God's presence for some people. They believed God would continue to be there for them no matter what happened in their lives and regardless of their illness or distress. A feeling of being loved unconditionally by God was particularly important to people who were socially isolated or lonely.

A few people believed in the power of God to help them or heal them in their distress. One person, for example, found his voices less harmful after prayer. Another believed that God would help her if she helped others.

RELIGIOUS AND SPIRITUAL BELIEFS AS 'MOST HELPFUL' STRATEGY

A few people gave their religious faith as one of the most helpful elements in their lives. As one person expressed it, religion could represent a complex mix of support, faith and spirituality. One person spoke of finding the fundamental peace in his life through his religious faith. Others spoke of the motivation to carry on the struggle, or of the meaning faith gave to an otherwise troubled life:

'Well, my Christianity is the foundation of my life.'

'That's what saves me every time, you know. I think I would probably have done something to myself by now if I hadn't got my faith.'

RECOMMENDATIONS

We recommend that
- **mental health professionals take a more holistic approach to mental health, and appreciate that individual treatments, therapies and services may be only a small part of the whole strategy adopted by someone living with mental health problems**
- **local authorities ensure equal access to sports and leisure facilities, and adult education, classes for people with mental health problems (for example, through training frontline staff, information to local statutory and voluntary mental health organisations, concessionary rates, targeted sessions)**
- **research organisations and funders prioritise further research in participation with service users, in order to find out more about the ways in which different activities are helpful to people**
- **local authorities ensure the implementation of Direct Payments legislation (as given in the Community Care (Direct Payments) Act 1996) in order to enable people with mental health problems to exercise more choice about the support they need when in distress**
- **mental health organisations disseminate information about the range of strategies that people find helpful, in order to assist people to find and develop their own strategies, and to locate alternative sources of help**

- **keyworkers provide people with the opportunity to include their particular strategy or strategies for coping as part of their care plan**
- **commissioners and purchasers of services, including Primary Care Groups, encourage the development of local self-help alternatives**
- **mental health service providers and professionals provide practical and administrative support to encourage the development of local self-help alternatives**
- **psychiatrist, GPs, CPNs, keyworkers and care managers provide information about local self-help alternatives to service users**
- **Care Programme Approach (CPA) mechanisms include the systematic collection and dissemination of people's personal coping strategies as part of the CPA process**
- **religious organisations of different faiths and denominations build bridges between themselves and work together to offer healing sanctuary to people with mental health problems of their own and other faith groups**
- **religious organisations and mental health service providers work together to improve awareness and communication on both sides, and to improve the care and treatment of people with mental health problems within a religious and spiritual context**
- **mental health workers raise their awareness of the core spiritual needs of all service users, and of the specific religious needs of service users of different ethnic and cultural groups**
- **user organisations, voluntary sector organisations and others develop stronger links with local religious organisations and provide information and guidance on mental health issues from a service user perspective.**

OTHER ACTIVITIES AND STRATEGIES

We could not cover in this report all of the different strategies or activities people mentioned during the course of their interviews. The following represents some of the many things we have not covered in any detail, but which had something to offer the people who used them – whether it be occupation, relaxation, meaning, love and affection, taking control, or symptom management.

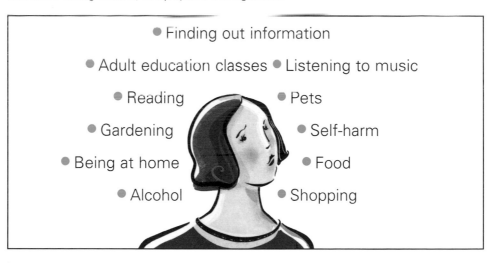

- Finding out information
- Adult education classes
- Listening to music
- Reading
- Pets
- Gardening
- Self-harm
- Being at home
- Food
- Alcohol
- Shopping

1   Read, J and Wallcraft, J (1992) *Guidelines for Empowering Users of Mental Health Services* Mind Publications/COHSE, London
2   Glenister, D (1996) *Exercise and Mental Health: A Review* Journal of the Royal Society of Health, February, pp. 7-13; cited in Wallcraft, J (1998) *Healing Minds* The Mental Health Foundation, London
3   Copsey, N (1997) *Keeping Faith: The provision of community health services within a multi-faith context* The Sainsbury Centre for Mental Health, London
4   Foskett, J (1999) *Soul searching within the service* Mental Health, Religion & Culture, 2 (1), 11-17
5   Mental Health Foundation (1999) *The Courage to Bare our Souls* Mental Health Foundation, London
6   Health Education Authority (1999) *Promoting Mental Health: The Role of Faith Communities – Jewish and Christian Perspectives* Health Education Authority, London

5 A summary of the most helpful supports and strategies

INTRODUCTION

This chapter gives an overview of the strategies, therapies, supports and activities identified as the most helpful or most important by the people we interviewed. Rather than attempt a summary of the whole report, we have chosen to explore here those elements that people valued most highly in their lives and the reasons they valued them in this way. In one of the early discussions with the interviewers, it was suggested that a key finding of the study might be that 'everyone is different'. It is certainly true that the complexity of things that people find helpful in their lives, and the reasons they do so, suggests infinite variety rather than any easy categorisation. However, some strong themes emerge across these differences that enable us to learn some general principles about living and coping with mental distress.

Table 8 gives an overall picture of the different strategies and supports people had found to be the 'most helpful' to them overall. Many people gave a combination of two or three supports, people, or activities, whilst a few found that one factor alone – or one person – stood out for them.

Table 8: 'Most helpful' strategies and supports	
Relationships with others • Friends • Other service users/people with similar problems • Mental health professionals • I feel accepted • Counsellors/therapists • People encountered in day centres, drop-ins, voluntary sector projects	*Medication*
	Physical exercise
	Religious and spiritual beliefs
	Money
Personal strategies • Peace of mind • Thinking positively, taking control	*Other activities* • Hobbies and interests • Information • Home • Creative expression

People talked about what they found 'most helpful' in slightly different ways, depending on where they were in relation to their illness or distress at the time of the interview. A number of people described the way in which the value placed on any form of support might vary over time. Different things could be helpful at different times, depending on the nature of change within the illness or distress, and also on the experience gained by the person. For example:

'It depends on, um, where you are with as a person in my illness. You know, if it's really, really bad, and I've got to go into hospital, what's helping me then is definitely my medication will help me. But... then, the [drop-in centre] helped me when I came out of hospital, kind of gave me that feel as though I belong somewhere, I could go somewhere where somebody was being friendly.'

So, the range of supports and strategies adopted can mean different things to people at different times and can have different roles to play in people's lives. The following broad categories help to describe these different roles, but also demonstrate the immense variation within those roles that could take place between individuals.

On-going survival strategies might include the value and significance of financial security, a sense of belonging and acceptance found in the company of like-minded people, work or daytime activities, physical exercise or the support of a religious faith. Taking control through personal and self-help strategies is another survival strategy, as is enjoyment found in a variety of different interests and activities.

Crisis or life-saving strategies might include contact with friends or professionals, medication and mental health services, the presence of children as a reason for living, the ethos of a religious faith, or an activity such as artistic expression or sport that can capture the attention away from self-destructive or negative thinking.

Symptom management might be achieved through the appropriate use of medication, through alternative strategies to control voice hearing, such as sport and physical exercise or listening to the radio or Walkman, and through strategies developed through talking therapies.

Healing strategies might be found through healing and complementary therapies, religious and spiritual beliefs, and through the development of personal strategies to achieve peace of mind.

The overwhelmingly predominant theme running through people's 'most helpful' supports was the role and value of relationships with other people, in all of their different forms. For some people, it was individuals, family or friends, whilst for others it meant the company of people encountered through local day centres or self-help groups (see Chapter 2). For still others, the important people in their lives were mental health professionals: counsellors or CPNs, support workers or social workers (see Chapter 3).

Another strong theme arising in relation to this question, was the importance of finding resources within oneself with which to deal with distress or mental health problems: finding ways of taking control of the distress through 'personal strategies'. As we see in Chapter 4, these strategies had often been developed from external sources of help and support, but had become internalised or 'owned' by people as they developed self-reliance or control over their distress.

One important issue that deserves attention is the relative absence of mental health services and treatments from this section. As we see in Chapter 3, mental health services and treatments played an important role in the lives of many people. Medication, when prescribed appropriately, could relieve symptoms and improve mood, and there were a number of mental health professionals who received special mention for the support and the services they provided. In this study, however, the 'most important' sources of help remained predominantly outside of the statutory mental health services. However, voluntary sector projects, some of them local Mind associations, some of them mental health projects serving African-Caribbean or Asian people, and some of them addressing particular life experiences such as sexual abuse, received enormous and grateful praise. Whilst this may be in some part due to the number of people recruited through voluntary sector projects, it is nevertheless worth noting that they were singled out for particular mention, for providing a vital lifeline for many people.

In order to understand the 'most helpful' issue in more depth, it is important for us to explore the reasons why these particular supports, people or activities were nominated as the most important, and to look for any common themes that occur across the different factors. Many of these issues have been explored in more detail in earlier chapters, so it is not for this chapter to explore them again in depth. Rather, we wish to understand why the particular strategies and supports given in the above table were highlighted as the most helpful elements in people's lives: what were the underlying themes to the value they placed on them, and whether any links could be found between them.

Common themes
- Acceptance
- Shared experience... shared identity
- Emotional support... 'being there'
- A reason for living
- Finding meaning... and purpose
- Peace of mind... and relaxation
- Taking control... having choices
- Security... and safety
- Pleasure

ACCEPTANCE

It is clear from listening to the people we interviewed that the stigma and discrimination experienced in relation to mental illness made the acceptance of others a vital element of their survival, and frequently a means of achieving self-acceptance. In Chapter 1, we see how many people found coming to terms with distress and diagnosis a long and difficult process. In Chapters 2 and 3, we see how the value and support, the affirmation and acceptance of others served for many as a valuable and vital route through that process, a lifeline to survival. The issue of stigma and discrimination has been highlighted elsewhere,[1] and most recently in the Mind inquiry report *Creating Accepting Communities*.[2] The interviews reported here suggest that many people experiencing mental distress seek out and create their own 'accepting communities', whether among friends or family, or among other people with similar experiences or a shared identity. Where they cannot do so, or are prevented from doing so, we can only reflect and affirm the isolation and social exclusion that result:

'[Drop-in] is like a safe haven really, from out there. Presumably there are some people a lot worse off than me – maybe mental health problems that will lead them to behave in very... unusual, unacceptable ways which result in them receiving derisive comments and ridicule. They have to suffer all that outside and in here they don't – they are just accepted for the person that they are, underneath the illness. That really is the key to it all here.'

SHARED EXPERIENCE... SHARED IDENTITY

Acceptance was very often found in the company of others who shared similar experiences, or who shared a key aspect of an individual's identity. Some people had discovered the value of shared experience through self-help groups addressing a particular aspect of mental distress, such as sexual abuse or depression, whilst others had discovered it through voluntary sector projects, drop-ins or day centres, where they had met 'like-minded' people. As much as the frequency with which this theme recurred, it was the strength and passion with which it was expressed that caused it to stand out for us. For some people, finding others who had experienced something similar to themselves was in itself important, because they had previously felt alone with their experiences, and now were able to find reassurance and affirmation of their experiences in the company of others.

There were additional issues of racial, cultural or sexual identity for some of the interviewees, which it was important for them to be sharing with the people from whom they sought help. This support was most frequently found through culturally specific voluntary sector projects, such as Asian or African-Caribbean day centres or projects. It is significant that many of the Asian and African-Caribbean people we interviewed had experienced very little, if any, help outside of these projects; as one Asian woman put it:

'Only [this project] has helped me. No-one else has ever helped me.'

EMOTIONAL SUPPORT... 'BEING THERE'

It was mainly named individuals who were identified as providing that most underestimated of functions: just 'being there'. This included mental health professionals who were available and accessible, people who listened and believed, and close members of the family or friends who had stayed with the person throughout a period or periods of distress. 'Being there' was more than just a physical presence, of course; it also meant a sense of safety or security for the person in distress, and a sense of being accepted 'warts and all':

'It's just that he's always, he's been there, and I know he's there for me, and it's just knowing he's there can help sometimes. I do know there is somebody at the end of that telephone.'

A REASON FOR LIVING

A few interviewees identified individual people in their lives, usually family and often children, as an important source of motivation to carry on with the struggle: perhaps because they felt needed as a carer or felt that they needed to be strong for the other person. This often arose in relation to children, but also in relation to a friend or relative who relied on the person being interviewed for care or support. One or two people identified their children as a reason for living, because of the hope they provided for the future or because they could lift them out of depression.

There were a number of other strategies and supports given as a reason for living. Religious and spiritual beliefs were often given as a fundamental belief system that provided meaning in people's lives and a reason to carry on through deep, and potentially suicidal, distress. One woman described her creative artistic activities as a vital lifeline, that had 'actually kept me alive' on more than one occasion.

FINDING MEANING... AND PURPOSE

A few people gave their religious faith as one of the most helpful factors in their lives. As one person expressed it, religion could represent a complex mix of support elements; it could be faith and spirituality, as well as the support of like-minded people. But one of the key underlying themes to having a religious faith was that it sustained people through giving meaning or purpose to their lives.

People could also find meaning in their lives through the care or support of others; often having been supported through their own illness or distress, they felt the need to provide help and support to others in return, to pass on their experience and knowledge, and this gave them a sense of purpose and value. Other people found purpose in their lives through employment or through other meaningful daytime activities, having something to get up for on a day to day basis being a sustaining element of a 'sense of purpose'.

PEACE OF MIND... RELAXATION

Several people spoke of the value of achieving peace of mind, whether simply through long experience or through other routes, such as religious or spiritual beliefs, or creative expression. These people had sought out an island of peace or quiet, or patience, within themselves that enabled them to live with their difficulties or to prevent further pressure or stress from affecting them within. For example, one man described his search for peace as a strategy for reducing stress, and related it to his religious belief.

Relaxation was achieved through physical or creative activities, music or complementary therapies (such as massage and aromatherapy) or through finding peace at home alone. Relaxation emerged as a strong theme in the *Knowing our own Minds* survey, where a range of alternative and complementary therapies were explored.

TAKING CONTROL... HAVING CHOICES

People found different ways of taking control of their distress or taking control of their lives. For some people, it had been vital to develop a positive attitude through self-help strategies. Their personal strategy for self-help had a proactive connotation, involving the encouragement or development of a mental or emotional state within themselves, a positive frame of mind or self-assertion to overcome negative thoughts or feelings (see Chapter 4). Some people had achieved greater control over their lives through taking a more proactive approach towards the treatments or therapies they used for their distress: for example, learning to self-medicate or using complementary therapies or alternative strategies within a self-help approach. Physical exercise had proved important to a number of people, through enabling them to take control over their physical and mental health and well-being.

An important aspect of taking control is being able to make choices. Some people talked about the importance of having access to appropriate information (for example, finding out information about their medication or diagnoses, or about alternatives to medication), and some talked of the importance of money in providing them with access to more choices in the strategies or activities they could adopt:

'Because [money] allows me to access everything else, without the money I would be... alone... would have to find a job, I can even stay in the flat I'm living in. So, I would say the money is the most important thing.'

SECURITY... AND SAFETY

Security could be emotional, physical and/or financial. For some people, finding a secure home had played an essential role in the development of their survival. Financial security was given as the most helpful factor in a couple of people's lives, because it enabled them to feel secure about their home and standard of living (and because it gave them access to other things – see above). The people who valued their home or money as a foundation for their strategy for living with distress, had either experienced homelessness or financial difficulty, learning by experience how essential are these basic factors:

'Because you know they're there, you often don't actually need to make that phone call, because you think... 'I feel safe'.'

Security could also be about feeling safe in the company of others, an emotional safety that enables trust to develop and distress to ease. Safety in this sense was most strongly highlighted by people who valued and sought the shared experience or shared identity of others; for example, lesbians and gay men, women who had been sexually abused, or people of African-Caribbean or Asian origin.

PLEASURE

Finally, we turn to the element of pleasure in people's lives. The concept of living with mental distress is inevitably presented as difficult and serious, as earnest and bleak. And of course, this is very often the case; as we have seen above, the stigma and discrimination associated with mental illness brings with it an extra layer of distress that makes life more difficult than ever to deal with. But, we should not also underestimate the fact that people can and do find pleasure in many things, and sometimes in the distress itself. In Chapter 1, we meet a couple of people who had become proud of their distress and their survival. There were also many people who described the pleasure they found in a range of different activities and interests, from creative and physical activities, through to gardening, reading and betting on the horses:

'Well it's, maybe, first on the list that helps me, having a bet on the horses, just watch them on television and that. I don't need to have a bet to enjoy them, like, you know. Watch them on the television and that, I enjoy that a terrible lot.'

RECOMMENDATIONS

We recommend that

- all mental health professionals, providers and policy makers recognise the expertise brought to the mental health field by the experience of mental health service users
- Government establish an Expert Patients Task Force in mental health, in order to build on that expertise to look at the role of people as experts in managing their distress; and to provide advice to the Chief Medical Officer on actions required to mainstream a programme of self-management of mental health problems
- Government reviews or replaces the Disability Discrimination Act (1995) with comprehensive anti-discrimination legislation based on a definition of disability that includes people with mental health problems
- Government and health education and health promotion agencies support the promotion of positive images of people living with mental health problems both locally and nationally, through a comprehensive anti-discrimination campaign
- all mental health professionals take a more holistic approach to mental health and appreciate that individual treatments and services may be only a small part of the whole strategy adopted by someone living with mental distress
- mental health providers and professionals recognise that everyone in distress is an individual and has different needs, preferences and potential ways of coping; and support their ways of coping through their inclusion in relevant care plans and reviews
- mental health organisations disseminate information about the range of strategies that people find helpful, in order to assist people to find and develop their own strategies, and to locate alternative sources of help
- commissioners and purchasers of services, including Primary Care Groups, encourage and promote the development of local self-help initiatives
- all mental health professionals provide information about local self-help groups, voluntary sector services, and user groups to service users
- mental health providers and professionals provide practical and administrative support to encourage the development of local self-help initiatives
- commissioners and purchasers of services encourage, fund and support the development of local black and minority ethnic voluntary sector projects in mental health
- Care Programme Approach mechanisms include the systematic collection and dissemination of people's personal coping strategies as part of the CPA process.

1   Rose, D (1996) *Living in the Community* Sainsbury Centre for Mental Health, London
2   Mind (1999) *Creating Accepting Communities* Mind Publications, London

INTRODUCTION

In the book *Doing Disability Research*,[1] Barnes and Mercer (1997) say that emancipatory research in the disability context should be enabling rather than disabling, and that it should be 'reflexive' and self-critical. For the research to be 'reflexive' we need to honestly examine the ways in which our identity as researchers affects the research we do and the interpretations we make of that research.

This chapter represents part of the reflexive approach we took to the *Strategies for Living* research, in engaging ourselves in reflecting upon the research and how we undertook it. We present the results of a discussion between the interviewers, followed by individual contributions from those who took part in the project, giving our own perspectives on the interviewing process, the people we interviewed and some of the painful and thought-provoking issues they raised.

Interviewing is not a neutral undertaking. It is an activity that usually takes place between two individuals, one of whom is the interviewer and the other the interviewee; one will ask the questions and the other will provide answers insofar as they are willing to do so. This sets up a situation where the two people are unequal for the purposes of the interviewing activity, but they may be unequal in other ways too. Perhaps the interviewer is paid to do the job, middle class, male and white, and perhaps the interviewee is female, unpaid, Asian and working class. There are many other possible differences and similarities between the two people, but there should always be an awareness of the power relationship established from the start of an interview.

One way of potentially reducing the strength of the power relationship between the 'researcher' and the 'researched' is for key aspects of their identity to be shared. In this project, all of the researchers, interviewers and interviewees shared one thing in common: their experience of mental distress and use of mental health services. Our research is as much about our own experiences as it is about the experiences of others,[2] in that we too are living with, or have lived with, mental distress. In this respect, disability research is following trends in social research where it has become commonplace to match interviewers to the interviewees' culture, ethnicity and/or gender. This does not remove the power differential between two people where one is the interviewer and the other the interviewee, but it challenges the conventional 'objective' approach to research. It accepts that our identities, as interviewers, can have an effect on the interviewing process.

The way in which the research project arose (out of the current concerns of mental health service users and survivors, but also within an established user-led framework at the Mental Health Foundation) also reflects our concern to challenge the social relations of research production, ie between the researchers and the researched, and, crucially, concerning who benefits from the research.

In addition, as users of mental health services, we and our interviewees may have had many difficult experiences of being 'interviewed' in the interests of mental health services, which add another potential layer of difficulty to the interview situation. In this project we wanted to know if we would be able to ameliorate this situation in any way, and enable people to open up about their experiences and views, by virtue of sharing some part of our interviewees' experience. We identified ourselves as users/survivors of mental health services in the information sent to the people we interviewed, and reiterated it as we introduced ourselves in person.

We also aimed to assure people that we were not simply gathering information from them, but were engaging them in a process of discovery and, hopefully, of constructive dissemination. We took additional information about the project to the interview, as well as a list of potential sources of help and advice, and we offered people the opportunity to be on our mailing list to receive our newsletter and information about the progress of the research. We also emphasised our aim that the information would be used to influence mental health services and professionals, and act as a resource for people with similar difficulties – with the aim of undertaking 'research where it will be of some practical benefit to the self-empowerment of disabled people and/or the removal of disabling barriers'.

We held a taped discussion midway through the interviewing process in which six of us – interviewers and researchers – took part in June 1998. These are some of the issues that arose from that discussion.

MENTAL HEALTH SERVICE USERS/SURVIVORS AS INTERVIEWERS – THE BENEFITS

A number of different issues arose in relation to this. All of the interviewers reported seeing people visibly relaxing or expressing relief when they realised that the interviewer had some experience of using mental health services. Some of the interviewers described having longer conversations with interviewees after the interview, where they revealed more about themselves, feeling that how we left people at the end of the interview was important – hopefully understood, possibly empowered by the experience:

'I'm fairly clear that it does make a difference from the beginning. I feel really good that this is being done in this way and that's how it should be, and like, one of them was saying to me 'I'd like to be doing this sort of thing some day' and so you feel that there's more kind of identification even if we don't give them any detail. I've experienced that with most of mine anyway.' – interviewer

The idea that there was more to the interviewing than an information gathering exercise was important to the interviewers: the belief that the research would prove to be a valuable resource in the future, and that they could communicate this to the interviewee. Another issue raised was the belief that, as service users, we were possibly less frightened than some researchers might be, by some of the more difficult issues arising from these interviews. Examples cited were talk of suicide and self-harm, and experiences like hearing voices or active delusions. This is not to say that we would not feel distressed by these, but that we might not shy away from them and would stay with and respect the person as an individual with those experiences.

We discussed the suggestion that, as people with experience of mental distress, and of using mental health services, we felt that we would ask different questions: that, the importance of service users designing and asking the questions was that we would get to the 'hidden issues'. As one interviewer put it, 'I think we've got more sense of what to look for'.

MENTAL HEALTH SERVICE USERS/SURVIVORS AS INTERVIEWERS – THE DIFFICULTIES

Difficulties arose for interviewers who found they had similar experiences to an interviewee. One or two felt that this caused them to probe less, either because they had a tendency to make assumptions, or because they felt too emotionally involved with the issue in question. For others, however, this caused them to probe or question more than usual in order to find out more about how this person had coped in a similar situation. Where different opinions were held to those expressed by an interviewee, perhaps about a particular coping strategy, there was sometimes a tendency to probe the issue rather less than otherwise. It may be that we were more reflexive and honest about such differences than is usual in social research. The training given at the start was praised for the preparation it gave people for dealing with assumptions, and the counterbalances it gave to some of these difficult situations.

RESPONSIBILITY

Some people felt a sense of responsibility for the interviewing – and for the money being invested in them by the Lottery and the Mental Health Foundation, and the additional pressure this put on them to do a good job. This sense of responsibility extended to the desire to prove that service users/survivors could be as good as anyone else at interviewing in social research.

DID WE GO FAR ENOUGH?

There was some discussion about whether the research had gone far enough in challenging the traditional researcher/researched relationship, and the power imbalance this entails. Did we, for example, make enough of the fact that we, too, had experience of mental distress? Or did we enter too much into the role of professional researcher and interviewer, and therefore not take sufficient advantage of the additional value we felt we had over other, more traditional, researchers? Several of the interviewers felt uncomfortable with the 'traditional power relationship' perpetuated through the interviewer role we were adopting. We had agreed that information shared before the interview would be confined to a simple statement, but that further discussion might take place after the interview when the interviewer could share as much about themselves as they wished. We were concerned that sharing too much information in advance of the interview might have a damaging effect, through influencing the interviewee's freedom to express their own views. Conversely, sharing too little might mean that the interviews would be no different from those of any other social researcher interviewing people with mental health problems. Different positions along this potential continuum may be adopted which involve lessening or increasing the gap between researcher and researched, interviewer and interviewee.

Furthermore, for those of us who were black or Asian interviewers, would we be seen as spies reporting on people from our communities to a predominantly white organisation? (see Colin King's contribution). This raises the issue of 'community knowledge' and how far people within a community wish to share their knowledge with 'other' or outside communities potentially seen as the enemy? This could apply to service users as well as to people from minority ethnic communities, or to women, etc.

We could perhaps have learned from other researchers who have adopted more flexible methods and looked more closely at the relevance of methods for the people we are and the people we were approaching for interview. At the time, one of our motivations was to ensure that our methodology would withstand scrutiny from a traditional academic research community, but methods are changing in the social research field, and perhaps with more confidence in the future, we might be able to reflect this in our own approach.

In the *Strategies for Living* research support project, we have supported six research projects, some of which have adopted more flexible approaches, including taped informal discussions over meals as well as group discussions and unstructured interviews, with the researcher taking a more participatory approach in many cases. For example, one researcher took part in the massage project she was investigating: giving and receiving massage herself, as well as interviewing people for their views on the experience. We shall be reflecting on these experiences in a future report.

CONTRIBUTIONS FROM THE INTERVIEWERS

REFLECTIONS ON USER-LED RESEARCH – HELEN BLACKWELL AND ELSIE LYONS

'...and that's how I cope'. I switched the tape-recorder off. Another interview completed, and yet again I'm left feeling exhausted and strangely humbled. These were the most frequent feelings at the end of any of the interviews we took part in as part of the project.

Asking people how they cope isn't quite the same as asking what brand of toothpaste they use. It stirs up a lot of personal feelings and experiences – more perhaps than for interviewers who haven't themselves 'been through the system'. Perhaps it says something about us that we felt an internal pressure to 'prove' that we could do it as well as the mainstream researchers.

So, what were the benefits of being user-researchers? Most people in the psychiatric system get very used to being asked questions – repeatedly – without really knowing what will happen to the information. People often said to us in the interviews 'this will be used to help other people, won't it?' Although we were still in control of the interview, in that we were exploring their various coping strategies, the balance of power felt very different. A shared experience of using the mental health system doesn't necessarily mean that we understand what someone else has gone through – but having this unwritten banner 'I've got a mental health problem' over one's head certainly engenders a feeling of solidarity, a mutual understanding of the way the world responds to us.

At the end of each interview we had to deal with our own feelings – memories – identification. Our ideas and ways of coping were challenged. Time and time again, we were struck by people's quiet dignity, strength and determination. We were humbled; we had been allowed to share in their journey.

User-led research is certainly a step forward but did we question the process enough? The interviews were structured around the way people coped with their mental health problems, but it was interesting that the one interviewee who had been in the mental health system longest was the one who said 'What problem?' We were also making assumptions. Perhaps we ought to do research on why people have a problem with us having a so-called problem!

Helen Blackwell
Elsie Lyons, 1999

MINA SASSOON

I wrote the following poem when trying to make sense of the 'coping strategies' used by the Asian women I interviewed for the *Strategies for Living* project. It touches upon the context within which ways of coping are chosen, the circumstances surrounding the choices made when faced with dire, often painful situations. It reflects my thoughts and my own observations on the often contradictory circumstances faced by many Asian women. I was both profoundly moved – as well as inspired – by the tremendous capacity for survival against the odds. Being of Asian origin myself, I found certain aspects of my own family life being reflected back to me, and echoes of the stories relayed to me over the years from within and outside of psychiatric services: the issues faced within the family and community; the issues faced when discrimination in many guises contributes to mental distress; the further despair caused when psychiatric services fail to understand the complexities – as well as our strengths. My poem attempts to capture the way in which all of these layers affect each other, and how cultural tradition, enshrined in deep-rooted values and judgements – about what is considered the right or wrong way of living our lives – can adversely affect mental health but can, ultimately, lead to a clearer view of what needs changing.

Dedicated to the Asian women I interviewed and to the community based organisations that helped them realise their strengths, 'Redefining the Code of Honour' explores the concepts of Izzat (pride/honour) and Sharam (shame) which pervade many an Asian woman's sense of identity.

Redefining the Code of Honour

> We're strong
> > We cope
> We struggle and survive
> > Against the odds
> Guiding everyone's lives
> > We're the carers
> the counsellors
> > the advisers
> the childbearers,
> > the homemakers
> the breadwinners
> > the dutiful wife and daughter.
> We ensure no shame befalls us
> > by close regard to others
> pushing aside our needs.
> > In the name of Honour.

> But what is this Honour?
> > And what is this shame?
> When all that we do
> > Is riddled with blame?
> When we're beaten
> > ...ignored
> > ...overlooked
> > ...and abused

When in trying to please everyone, we end up confused.
    And we're told....
'You must try harder to be more demure,
    to be more respectful, considerate and pure.
To keep the kids quiet, to keep the house clean,
    to put up with ill-temper, put up with the scenes.'
In the name of Honour.

So back to our duties, trying harder each time,
    to be how tradition defines us...
and ourselves we blame.

But when the struggle defeats us
    and we cry out in pain,
we get labelled psychotic, depressed and insane.
    Prescribed pills to numb us by the family GP
And we silently wonder 'is this a conspiracy?'

But if we dare voice this,
    we're called paranoid.
So sink slowly, and deeper
    back into the void.

We dare not take our problems outside,
    for this too, is taboo.
So we silently wonder 'what are we to do?'
    the institutions meant to help in times of distress
just reinforce our alienation, just add to our stress.

They only blame our culture, tell us to escape and
    break out.
They just don't understand what it's all about.
    For in a society where racism is rife,
yes – an oppressed man, for example, may take it
    out on his wife.
But it's not that simple, so many layers to explore:
    when a community exists within a climate of hostility,
oppressions within it, often rise to the fore.

But my message to you all here today is that...
    Pain can, and does lead to transformation,
the openings of pathways never before considered.
    When things get tough, our personal resources
show themselves.

Take stock of your achievements, no matter how small
    they appear to you
Reach out to each other, we're our own best resource,
    as women we're creative, together a strong force.
Explore your feelings, your desires and dreams.
We can redefine the code of honour –
    based on our needs.

Today is our day and so be all our tomorrows.
    Make time for yourselves, time to play and be joyful
Explore what's available, build up a network of support
Yes – we'll still be strong and nurturing
    But we'll no longer take all this blame.

Mina Sassoon © March 1999

USER PERSPECTIVE ON INTERVIEWING BLACK PEOPLE WITH MENTAL HEALTH RELATED DIFFICULTIES – COLIN KING

Being Mad

> I like to introduce myself, Mr Insane, subnormal
>   and psychotic.
> In England I'm Mr Dangerous, difficult and threatening.
>   In my family, I'm a brother, son, Uncle and Friend.
> At school I'm educationally subnormal, delicate
>   and confused.
> At college I'm angry, distant and maintain a
>   white free zone.
> In my dreams I'm brave, famous, knowledgeable
>   and articulate.
> In my writings ineligible and badly presented.
>   In my verbal, mumbled, soft and unarticulated.
> In public places I'm your potential robber and mugger.
> At police stations, abused, heart problems,
>   potential death case.
> With black people, approachable, loved, appreciated
>   and understood.
> With white people, cultural misfit, colourless
>   and maladjusted.
> With white women, a sexual objectification of pleasure.
>   With white men, masculine, penis orientated, feared.
> In hospital, overly medicated, controlled
>   and misunderstood.
> On the ward, no rights, no identity, an object of theory.

The purpose of the interviews

I was employed on a temporary contract by the Mental Health Foundation as an interviewer, to use my experiences as a mental health survivor, to conduct a number of interviews with people with a history of mental illness to look at what helped them cope.

The aim of the project was to talk to a cross-section of service users from different regions, sexual, racial and cultural backgrounds. I was the only black man of African and Caribbean origin interviewing, and interviewed service users of similar race classification. This decision followed on from a great deal of group discussions involving four white women and one Asian woman, about the emotional, professional and personal issues in terms of race matching, and cross-cultural dynamics in eliciting personal information.

From the start of this process I communicated my feelings of not wanting to be abused as a 'black male spy', for the purposes of a white organisation. My aim in this project was to ensure that the confidentiality of black users was preserved, both professionally and politically, and that the information obtained should not be used to reinforce historical stereotypes around black people in mental health and psychiatry.

Content of the interviews

I like to reflect both factually and emotionally on the experiences of a three hour journey on a train, to a black mental health project in the Midlands, to talk to six black users, two women and four men, about their personal stories, and the specific support and ways that they coped with the potential of a mental health breakdown.

I want to respect the detailed individual information of the service users and pay attention to some of the common issues of context that emerged from the interviews. To set the context, all interviews took place in the same room, a small room attached to the main project. It held two seats, quite close together, grey carpet, light grey walls with pictures of significant black icons (Bob Marley, Nelson Mandela, and Diane Abbott). It was a room of warmth, symbolic of a black space, a space away from the close clinical setting of a mental health hospital.

I remember the homely welcome of the Project Manager, and people waiting to see me, to talk, to be heard, but more essentially to be paid. Each interviewee was given £15 for their time, they were all asked similar questions, about their diagnosis, their family and personal support, their community, and the specific therapies and community supports that enabled them to survive.

Most of those interviewed were surprised I had survived the system, they almost related to me as Fanon, their survivor, the need to look more closely at the person, within the context of the political and the racial.

One of the recurring themes in the interview was a disabling sense of loss, of a life that was now dead and could not be returned to. When going through the list of community supports, most thought they had been unhelpful and almost penal, the statutory procedures made them feel dehumanised.

In terms of their diagnosis, many didn't understand it, how it was constructed, but they remembered the patronising way it was communicated to them, which objectified their reality under very rigid labels. A few spoke of a sense of being dragged, pulled, arrested, in the process of being taken to hospital. The echo of slavery rings loud in the way these painful encounters were discussed.

Most of the service users talked as if this was normal treatment, and internalised the stereotype ('maybe it was something wrong with me'). This stigma reverberated as an essential part of their identity, one young black man sadly reflecting: 'I didn't deserve any better'.

When talking about their homes, their family, their sense of community attachment and support, this was set and established around the networks they had built up whilst at the black mental health project. Some talked as if family and friends had died, as they were seen as abnormal and diseased, potentially infectious; notions of being in relationships were completely redundant, the project became central, explicit and a sacred part of their existence.

The professionals they encountered became symbolic of the danger, people who could do them damage, people who came into their homes once a month insincere in their static questioning, invading them with a needle, medication, and then threatening them with a return to the hospital if they deteriorated.

I think the last and most pertinent theme, when talking about the list of alternative therapies that helped people cope with stress, with the exception of counselling, few had heard, been offered or tried the therapies listed. An important and consistent theme is that most people thought that any therapy would be more beneficial if the person providing the therapy was of the same racial and cultural origin.

Ethical problems

The issues for black researchers, reliving their own pain through the descriptive of the users of similar histories and cultural experiences. This can polarise the role of black researchers between giving information to white institutions or becoming a political activist in clearly representing the much marginalised voice of this group.

The specific gender issues in talking to black women and black men, an appeal to their specifically different histories, both politically and morally.

The interview has the potential to replicate the approaches adopted by the statutory agencies, potentially invasive, rigid questioning, that creates racial tensions with black clients.

The purchase for the insight of blackness, through the payment of £15, can have different connotations in relation to a client group who have become so deprived and abused, and then come to see such payment as a reward for their painful disclosures.

The importance of preparing for talking to black people, particularly in relation to the order of questions, use of words, place and context, and the sensitivity of recording, points to a need for a culturally sensitive approach to research.

Colin King, September 1999

HEARING EACH OTHER'S STORIES – JAN WALLCRAFT

It was my task as full-time researcher with *Strategies for Living* to set up and co-ordinate the interviews, as well as to do a share of the interviews myself. I was concerned to ensure that we learned as much from the research process as from the interviews, as user-led research in mental health is still a very new area, which has yet to be mapped out. We took and adapted a particular model of qualitative research, but I think that the skills we brought to the task came from our personal experiences as much as from our training and work experience. Each interview was unique and different, and the guidelines we were working to had to be interpreted flexibly.

On the train coming back from one interview I read the following description of how people meet and interact in 'Emotional Intelligence' by Daniel Coleman:

'... there's a dance, a synchrony, a transmission of emotions. This mood synchrony determines whether you feel an interaction went well or not.'

This is a good description of what I experienced in my interviews. Each was like a roller-coaster ride during which I shared in people's journeys of survival. For some, the dominant emotion was anger, perhaps at the treatment they had received when they sought help, or even when they didn't feel they needed help at all. For others, it was sad resignation; making the best of what was still possible. But for most, the overriding impression I received was of the courage with which people had kept on picking themselves up and fighting to overcome their problems, using whatever help came their way in constructing their own emotional rescue plan.

Perhaps because we interviewed people mostly at voluntary sector mental health projects, these featured strongly in people's coping strategies. However, I noted especially how important it was to have found a secure haven and a support network, whether this represented home and family, drop in centre or church, or an activity that renewed hope of growth and change, such as education, training, work or religious practice. Psychiatric diagnosis and medication was rarely seen as a key factor in coping, and for many this was experienced as an additional burden.

The first interview I carried out was one of the most challenging. I was welcomed to a cosy family home where an elderly woman described her painful and unfinished journey through many years of distress and psychiatric treatment, beginning in her youth. She was clearly reassured to know that I had experienced treatment myself, and wanted to know more about me. I promised to answer all her questions afterwards, which I did, and we were able afterwards to dismantle the artificial barriers of the formal interview. This didn't happen in every interview, but it was always a possibility, and I always felt that some genuine sharing and interaction had taken place.

It was clear in this and many other interviews that although modern mental health services were generally less harsh and punitive than those of 20 years ago, they were still failing people and often damaging them. As a researcher, it wasn't my role to help people resolve their problems. I found this frustrating, but I hoped that being heard and knowing they were contributing to something that could help others had some healing value. Many of the people I interviewed did express their wish to contribute to understanding and better services, and this increased my sense of obligation to report their words faithfully. Sometimes identifying too strongly with interviewees was a problem. I found that with one person who suffered a similar problem to my own I was reluctant to keep asking for more detail. Perhaps someone more distant from the problem might have managed this better. However, I felt that the interview worked, because simply listening with understanding gave her the space to go into greater depth without too much prompting.

Because in each project we visited people who had been asked to volunteer to be interviewed, it was inevitable that a proportion would be those who were active in self-help or collective involvement. Whether or not these were representative, it was a bonus to talk to some people who had reflected on how their problems had originated and developed clear views on what types of therapy worked for them.

The life stories that I witnessed: tales of disaster, courage and mutual support, were far more interesting and enlightening than those in many TV programmes. I found myself wishing that someone would be brave enough to make a TV series based on the genuine experiences of mental health service users, involving people like our interviewees as programme consultants. This would cut through the misinformation about us in the media and help to create genuine understanding of us as fellow human beings. Hearing each others' stories without criticism or judgement is something we rarely have time to do; it was a privilege to be able to do this work, and I hope that this report encourages many others involved in mental health to talk and to listen to each other.

Jan Wallcraft, 1999

RESEARCHING THE RESEARCHED – ALISON FAULKNER

As a researcher for something like fourteen years, I have often felt ambivalent about the research or the interviewing that I have been involved in. I remember trying to interview one or two people in hospital when they had only recently been admitted under section 136 of the Mental Health Act (1983). I felt deeply inadequate to the situation as well as being aware of how inappropriate it felt to be interviewing 'captive' people despite having gained their apparent consent. Similarly I remember interviewing a man in his own home about his employment history, and job-seeking activities. He asked me, as I sat there in my neat clothes with my tape recorder and briefcase, whether I had a job for him. 'well, do you?'.

I also remember, when in a therapeutic community some twenty years ago, the community group being asked for our consent to a video being taken of a morning session for one of the therapist's research. For some years afterwards, I worried about what had happened to that video: where it had ended up and who had seen it. We gave our consent, but more out of a sense of resignation or fear of speaking out than any real agreement.

As a user of mental health services, it has often concerned me that researchers and mental health professionals often have the worst stereotyped images of what it is to be a service user, and have difficulty accepting that we might have skills and abilities far beyond our use of services. I was once interviewed by a medical student who, when told that I had a psychology degree, responded by saying 'well done!'.

It seemed to me that this research offered an opportunity for us to do things differently, to build on and to share our skills and expertise – in both research and in mental distress – in order to bring about a body of knowledge valuable ultimately to other people experiencing mental distress. Of course, 'intent is no guarantee of outcome',[4] but hopefully this report is a contribution to the work of a great many service users and survivors striving to find alternative and more powerful 'strategies for living' than those offered by conventional mental health services.

Alison Faulkner, 1999

1   Barnes, C and Mercer, G (1997). *Doing Disability Research* The Disability Press, Leeds
2   See also: Vernon, A (1997) *Reflexivity: the dilemmas of researching from the inside* in Barnes and Mercer (eds) (1997) *Doing Disability Research* The Disability Press, Leeds; Beresford and Wallcraft (1997) *Psychiatric System Survivors and Emancipatory Research: issues, overlaps and differences* in Barnes and Mercer (above)
3   Priestley, M *Whose Research?: A personal audit* in Barnes, C and Mercer, G (1997) *Doing Disability Research* The Disability Press, Leeds
4   Barton, L (1996) *Disability and Society: emerging issues and insights* Longman, London. Quoted in Vernon, A (above)

UNSATISFIED NEEDS AND SERVICE GAPS

The interviews explored with people what factors they felt were missing from their strategies for living with distress, whether related to services or to other areas of their lives. This brief afterword provides us with some insight into the needs people felt remained unmet, or the services they felt they would benefit from.

Someone to talk to

The strongest theme to emerge was the need for someone to talk to, usually in times of crisis and frequently when in hospital. This reinforces one of the strongest messages to emerge from *Knowing our own Minds*, where the majority of people said that this was the one thing they most wanted or needed when in distress. It is something we see expressed time and time again, particularly in relation to in-patient care.[1,2] Here, people talked of different contexts where having someone to talk to would be helpful. One or two people expressed the wish for nursing staff to take the initiative and offer the space and time in which to talk:

'I was told I could go and see the nurse if I wanted to talk, but the way I felt I couldn't go and see anybody. So I'd have liked it if the nurse had come to me and had a set time or something like that to sort of discuss things... in the hospital setting. I think a lot of patients wanted that, they wanted to talk but there was no-one there to talk to.'

A particular need, expressed by several people, was to be given time with a professional to have things explained to them – about their diagnosis, treatment and other issues relating to their care. This was something they felt they had picked up gradually or by chance, and still felt no-one had taken time to explain things to them properly:

'I would have found it much more helpful if someone had actually sat down with me and explained whatever happened to me, how I got to hospital, what they thought was wrong with me, and how they envisaged life going on for me, would have given me some sense of how was my condition.'

Talking therapies

A few people said that they would like access to a talking therapy, or that they would have liked it at a time when they had only been offered drugs or admission to hospital. In some cases, this was indistinguishable from the need for someone to talk to. However, one or two people were clear about this being a different issue, such as the woman who wished that she and her husband had been offered relationship counselling at a time when it might have helped them.

Crisis/out of hours services

Several people felt the need for more easily accessible services in a crisis, particularly out of normal office hours or emergency care overnight:

'I feel there should be a bit more out there for people in crisis situation, that's the strong feeling I have, there should be more help when somebody who's going seriously ill, there should be a hand there for somebody to reach out and hold, and not be left to just carry on.'

Complementary therapies

Quite a few people, who had found complementary therapies helpful, said that they would like easier access to, and greater availability of, complementary therapies. There were two different issues under consideration here: one was the need for mental health services and the NHS in general, to recognise the value of complementary therapies and hence make them easily available. The other was the simple matter of the cost of private treatments, prohibitive to most people living on benefits:

'I wish aromatherapy, and massage definitely, could be done on the mental health service... especially [for] patients on high doses of medication that makes them physically stiff and uncomfortable.'

Practical support

Many people expressed the need for more practical support. For some people, this was support to enable them to live at home more successfully – help with benefits and finance, and help with practical aspects of keeping a home. One or two others mentioned other specific contexts, such as practical help at school, or support with caring for children when they were experiencing a crisis. Finally a couple of people wanted support to enable them to go out more, as they found it difficult to leave the house without encouragement:

'... just another human being to, er, help me with the bits and pieces of living, in the sense of, you know... sorting out debts and have I cleaned the place...'

Services for black and minority ethnic people

Several of the people we interviewed who were attending and benefiting from Asian or African-Caribbean voluntary sector projects felt there should be more of them, or easier access to them for other people:

'They understand, they understand... when you're in your own space, if you want to call it that, or you're in your own place, you can do what you want, you know, and it obviously does make a difference – the things that the National Health Service can't provide – this, this filled the gap.'

...And a greater awareness

Several people talked of the need for greater awareness amongst mental health professionals, about the issues affecting people from minority ethnic, cultural or religious groups. One person told a story about a friend that demonstrated ignorance amongst hospital nurses about the need for Kosher food.

Another said that her experience of life and mental health would have been different if racism had been acknowledged from an early age. She said that, if she had been able to talk to someone about it:

'It would've definitely helped me to sort myself out... definitely helped me to clear my head... It's not easy to make friends sometimes and racism certainly has something to do with making friends.'

Advocacy and user involvement

A couple of people felt there should be more user involvement in their local services, and advocacy for people who needed it:

'[There should be] more users involved – folk that know what it's like to be ill, and what it feels like to be under stress... but that involves training people as well, and there needs to be some training for people and nobody climbing in at the deep end, like I was.'

More understanding from employers

One person, speaking from personal experience felt strongly that employers lacked understanding about mental health problems amongst their employees:

'I don't think that employers are that sympathetic towards people who suffer from depression. [They] are very often good workers, conscientious and... there is no reason why they can't be a good member of the team working. I think there is a lot of lack of understanding, to do with stigma.'

AND FINALLY...

The final word goes to a woman who said that, before the research interview, she had never before been asked for her feelings or opinions about care or treatment:

'Nobody has ever sort of asked my opinion on anything like this before, you know – how I feel about anything. It's all within the psychiatrist's room, and you have to agree with what he says, and that's it, sort of thing.'

1   Sainsbury Centre for Mental Health (1999) *Acute Problems: a survey of the quality of care in acute wards* The Sainsbury Centre for Mental Health, London
2   Faulkner, A (1998) *Experts by experience* Mental Health Nursing, 18(4), pp.6-8

APPENDIX A

STRATEGIES FOR LIVING ADVISORY COMMITTEE

Marion Beeforth (Chair)

Hanif Bobat, Awaaz Asian Mental Health Project, Manchester

Roberta Grayley/Andrew Wetherell, UK Advocacy Network

Elcena Jeffers, African-Caribbean Users and Survivors Forum

Doris Kempe, Depression Alliance

Brian McDonald, MindLink

Ros Newnham, Manic Depression Fellowship

Gill Rigby, UKAN

Lynda Smith (formerly of African-Caribbean Mental Health Association)

Ecid Somers, MindLink Wales (formerly Wales Us Network)

APPENDIX B

LOCAL CONTACTS FOR INTERVIEWEES

Many thanks to:

Inderjit Bans, Tasha Foundation

Hanif Bobat, Awaaz Asian Mental Health Project, Manchester

Marilyn Bryant, Awetu (Black Mental Health Project) Cardiff

Marie Burns, Glasgow Association for Mental Health

Yasmin Choudhry, QALB Centre, London

Nick Dent, Canterbury Users Forum

Alicia Gordon, African Caribbean Community Initiative, Wolverhampton

Stephen Hill, Coventry MIND

Billy McCloud, Ayr Action for Mental Health

Jennifer Miller, Bradford Advocacy Project

New Town Centre, Birmingham

M Ryder, Beechcroft Centre, Birmingham

Mina Sassoon, Core Arts, London

Marilyn Scott, Arvon (Bangor) Mind

Mrs Scougall, Edinburgh Association for Mental Health

Yvonne Singleton, Jephcott House, Coventry

Fiona Taylor, Birmingham MIND

Mike Taylor, CAB Mental Health Project, Weston Super Mare

...and anyone else we have missed out

APPENDIX C

INTERVIEW TOPIC GUIDE OUTLINE

Opening and introduction

Section 1: Personal circumstances
- living circumstances, age, ethnic origin, employment status, physical health

Section 2: Mental health problems and past psychiatric treatment
- mental health problems in own words; diagnosis and feelings about it

Section 3: Living and coping with mental health problems
- current psychiatric treatments and supports
- other treatments, supports and therapies
- personal, social, and leisure interests
- housing, environment, health and work
- religious and spiritual beliefs

Section 4: Summary, and suggestions or advice to other people
- most helpful/most important strategies or supports
- advice to others

Close

SOURCES OF HELP

Key mental health organisations

African-Caribbean Mental Health Association
49 Effra Road
Suite 37
London SW2 1BZ
020 7737 3603
email: acmha1@aol.com

Chinese Mental Health Association
Oxford House
Derbyshire Street
London E2 6HG
020 7613 1008
email: admin@cmha.demon.co.uk

Confederation of Indian Organisations
5 Westminster Bridge Road
London SE1 7XW
020 7928 9887

Depression Alliance
35 Westminster Bridge Road
London SE1 7JB
Helpline: 020 7633 9929
email: hq@depressionalliance.org
www.depressionalliance.org

Depression Alliance Cymru
11 Plas Melin
Westbourne Road
Whitchurch
Cardiff CF4 2BT
02920 692891

Depression Alliance Scotland
3 Grosvenor Gardens
Edinburgh EH12 5JU
0131 467 3050

Eating Disorders Association
1st Floor
Wensum House
103 Prince of Wales Road
Norwich NR1 1DW
Under 19's Helpline: 01603 765050, Mon-Fri 4pm-6pm
Helpline: 01603 621414, Mon-Fri 9am-6.30pm

Fellowship of Depressives Anonymous
Box FDA
Ormiston House
Self Help Nottingham
32-36 Pelham Street
Nottingham NG1 2EG
Helpline: 01702 433838

Hearing Voices Network
91 Oldham Street
Manchester M4 1LW
0161 834 5768
email: hearingvoices@care4free.net

Manic Depression Fellowship
Castleworks
21 St Georges Road
London SE1 6ES
020 7793 2600
email: mdf@mdf.org.uk

Mental Health Foundation
20/21 Cornwall Terrace
London NW1 4QL
020 7535 7474
email: mhf@mentalhealth.org.uk

MIND (National Association for Mental Health)
Granta House
15-19 The Broadway
London E15 4BQ
020 8519 2122
Information line: Mon-Fri 9.15am-4.45pm
0845 766 0163 (outside London); 020 8522 1728 (inside London)

MIND Cymru
3rd Floor
Quebec House
Castlebridge
Castlebridge Road East
Cardiff CF1 9AB
01222 395123

MINDlink (MIND's network of service users)
address as for MIND, above

National Schizophrenia Fellowship
28 Castle Street
Kingston upon Thames
Surrey KT1 1SS
Advice line: 020 8974 6814
email: info@london.nsf.org.uk
www.nsf.org.uk

National Voices Forum (NSF's network of service users)
address as for National Schizophrenia Fellowship, above

The Samaritans
10 The Grove
Slough SL1 1QP
Helpline: 0345 909090
Administration: 01753 532713

Scottish Association for Mental Health
Cumbrae House
15 Carlton Court
Glasgow G5 9JP
0141 568 7000
email: enquire@samh.org.uk

Survivors Speak Out
34 Osnaburgh Street
London NW1 3ND
020 7916 5472

Turning Point
New Loom House
101 Backchurch Lane
London E1 1LU
020 7702 2300
email: turningpointmail@turning-point.co.uk
   Helps people with drink, drug and mental health problems

UK Advocacy Network
14-18 West Bar Green
Sheffield S1 2DA
0114 272 8171
email: ukan@can-online.org.uk

Other useful contacts

Abuse in therapy
Prevention of Professional Abuse Network (POPAN)
1 Wyvil Court
10 Wyvil Road
London SW8 2TG
020 7622 6334
email: popan@easynet.co.uk
   Campaigns against professional misconduct; supports individual complaints against therapists

Co-counselling
There are local contacts for co-counselling groups and courses in most areas; you could try looking in your local telephone book or local library, or contact adult education institutions in your area.

Counselling and psychotherapy
The British Association for Counselling
1 Regent Place
Rugby
Warwickshire CV21 2PJ
01788 578328
www.counselling.co.uk

Westminster Pastoral Foundation
23 Kensington Square
London W8 5HN
020 7361 4800
www.wpf.org.uk

British Confederation of Psychotherapists
37 Mapesbury Road
London NW2 4HJ
020 8830 5173
The BCP compiles a register of psychoanalytic psychotherapists; and also publishes a leaflet called Finding a Therapist

Lesbians and gay men

PACE
34 Hartham Road
London N7 9JL
Main switchboard: 020 7700 1323
Advocacy line: 020 7697 0017
email: pace@dircon.co.uk
Counselling service for lesbians and gay men

Medication and ECT

ECT Anonymous
14 Western Avenue
Riddlesden
Keighley
West Yorkshire BD20 5DJ
01535 661493, Tue & Wed 10am-4pm; Thurs 10am-2pm
email: ect.anon@ndirect.co.uk

CITA (Council for Involuntary Tranquilliser Addiction)
Cavendish House
Brighton Road
Liverpool L22 5NG
Helpline: 0151 949 0102
www.liv.ac.uk/~csunit/community/cita.htm

UKPPG (UK Psychiatric Pharmacy Group Medical Helpline)
South London and Maudsley NHS Trust
Denmark Hill
London SE5 8AZ
020 7919 2999 (for users of mental health services)
020 7703 5411 (for mental health practitioners)

See also MIND's Information Line (above) information about psychiatric drugs is given, but they cannot give medical advice.

For more information about your medication, you could try contacting your local pharmacist.

Women's therapy

Women's Therapy Centre
10 Manor Gardens
London N7 6JS
020 7263 6200, Mon-Thurs 10am-12 noon, 2pm-4.30pm; Fri 10am-12 noon
email: info@womenstherapycentre.co.uk